Stomp Rockets, Catapults & Kaleidoscopes

Stomp Rockets, Rockets, Catapults & Kaleidoscopes

30+ Amazing Science Projects You Can Build For Less Than $1!

by Curt Gabrielson

STERLING INNOVATION

New York

STERLING INNOVATION
New York

An Imprint of Sterling Publishing Co., Inc.
1166 Avenue of the Americas
New York, NY 10036

ISBN 978-1-4351-3006-7

Distributed in Canada by Sterling Publishing Co., Inc.
c/o Canadian Manda Group, 664 Annette Street
Toronto, Ontario, Canada M6S 2C8
Distributed in the United Kingdom by GMC Distribution Services
Castle Place, 166 High Street, Lewes, East Sussex, England BN7 1XU
Distributed in Australia by NewSouth Books
45 Beach Street, Coogee, NSW 2034, Australia

For information about custom editions, special sales, and premium and corporate purchases,
please contact Sterling Special Sales at 800-805-5489 or specialsales@sterlingpublishing.com.

Manufactured in China

8 10 9

www.sterlingpublishing.com

Interior design by Monica Baziuk

**To the kids of Watsonville, California.
Here's to many more years of great ideas
and science projects!**

ACKNOWLEDGMENTS

I HAD THE PRIVILEGE of working with many fine people to make this book happen. Juan Jose Padilla and Lorena Onofre of our Students Teaching Project shot and posed for many of the photos. Gustavo Hernandez, my assistant extraordinaire, shot and posed for many photos, did a lot of editing, and kept hundreds of projects and parts organized in our cramped space. Araceli and Frankie Ortiz and Erick Torres also helped with some photos.

Paul Doherty of the Exploratorium Teacher Institute kindly proofed these activities for content, and Pat Murphy in Exploratorium Publications (and of the Brazen Hussies!) gave a lot of useful advice.

Much appreciation goes to my wise superiors in the City of Watsonville's Department of Public Works and Utilities—Tami Stolzenthaler, Nancy Lockwood, Bob Geyer, David Koch—and also to Carol Thomas and Al Smith, all of whom gave great support for this book. Thanks also to Watsonville city manager Carlos Palacios and the city council for all their support of the Watsonville Environmental Science Workshop past and future. Finally, thanks for the support and ideas from other community science workshop directors across the country.

Most of the ideas here originated or were significantly developed by students and staff at the Watsonville Environmental Science Workshop. Like folk tunes, science projects such as these are constantly being changed and improved upon as they pass from hand to hand, shop to shop. I've given credit within the chapter for ideas that I recall picking up from a distinct person or place, whether or not that was the true origin.

CONteNtS

✳ Electricity and Magnetism

✳ Sound, Light, and Perception

✳ Mechanics

✳ Fluids and Aerodynamics

✳ Biology

✳ Chemistry

Appendixes

iNtRODuctiON

ALL NATURAL THINGS—SOLAR SYSTEMS, volcanoes, glaciers, tornadoes, camels, live oak trees, sea turtles, algae, cardiovascular systems, silicon nuclei—just work, without any human effort. On the other hand, most of the gadgets that you use each day, both high and low tech, have been *made* to work by people. When you cry out "It doesn't work!" you should remember that *not* working is actually a gadget's default condition.

To make something work is exceptional—it takes know-how and ingenuity. Ten thousand years ago, every family knew more or less how to make everything work that was necessary for their existence: where to find the materials, how to put them together, how to use the finished product. People in many so-called backward places in the world can still do this today. But here in our "advanced" society, where we're up to our ears in technology? I challenge you to think of three things you depend on daily that you could create from scratch, even given all the materials set out in front of you. We are clearly losing our touch.

This book will show you how to build more than 30 amazing science toys. You will learn a lot as you build them, about science and about making things work. You can work with friends or alone. Adults are helpful to have around, but don't let them take over your project!

You can build these toys in any order, and don't feel like you have to follow these directions precisely. If you do, you'll end up with a fine working project, but if you can see a better way to do it, go for it. The toys here are all open-ended, so you can keep on going and make more amazing stuff. In fact, many of these projects were developed from kids' ideas. If you come up with a brilliant idea in the process of building these projects, send it to me. I probably won't make you rich and famous, but I'll pass your idea on to thousands of other kids, who will then have a chance to improve it even more.

The toys here will cost you about 75¢ each. If you can't squeeze that out of your parents, you need to work on your technique. Many of the materials you'll need you can get for free from a garbage can or recycling bin or find lying around the house. To get a few of the materials, you may have to go to a specialty shop or order them from a catalog or over the Internet. Some sources are listed at the end of Appendix A, "Bringing These Projects into the Classroom."

You'll need some basic tools to construct these toys. Definitely get your parents to help you gather these tools—don't just help yourself to your mom's tool cabinet. The most complex tool required in these projects is a hand drill. If you have a thick piece of wood or several pieces fastened together for a drill platform, the projects can be done on any table without damaging the surface. Several of the projects should be done outside, owing to noise or messiness. Here's a list of common tools you may need for these projects. Each project will have a list of any additional special tools you will need.

TOOLBOX

✳ Knife	✳ Hot glue gun (low-temperature models work fine and are much safer)
✳ Side cutters	
✳ Needle-nose pliers	✳ Hot glue sticks (plenty!)
✳ Scissors	✳ Markers or paint
✳ Ruler	✳ Decorations of various kinds
✳ File	✳ Masking tape
✳ Scraper	✳ Black tape
✳ Hacksaw	✳ Duct tape
✳ Wood saw	✳ Hand drill with variable speed
✳ Vise or C-clamp	✳ At least these drill bits: $15/64$-inch,* $19/64$-inch,* $1/2$-inch
✳ Flat-blade screwdriver	
✳ Phillips screwdriver	✳ A few nails to serve as tiny drill bits ("nail bits")
✳ Hammer	

* Dowels of $1/4$ inches and $5/16$ inches are used in many projects and often inserted into holes. If you make a hole $1/64$ of an inch smaller than the dowel, then hammer the dowel in, it will fit nice and tightly. This is also a good opportunity to practice your fractions: $1/4 - 1/64 = 15/64$ and $5/16 - 1/64 = 19/64$.

You'll also want a few boxes to store materials and tools in; then when you go to work on future projects, you'll have all sorts of supplies ready at hand. If possible, you'll want to set up all your stuff in a corner with a table or workbench where you don't have to clean it up each time you stop working. It's an adult secret I'll clue you in on right now: real scientists and engineers and artists hardly *ever* clean up—they just organize the mess in the direction of the next project. You can quote me on that.

Finally, remember, **SAFETY IS FIRST!** What kind of fun will you have if you rip a big gash in your finger or poke a hole in your eye? Always be careful, and never joke around when it comes to safety.

Building things is great fun. Making things work and fixing things are not only satisfying but also can save you money and teach you all kinds of stuff in interesting ways. You may not get much of a chance to do these sorts of things at school these days, but you shouldn't be waiting for school to teach you what you want to know anyway.

Happy building!!

A Note to Adults

The projects in this book do not include laboratory exercises, structured discovery lessons, or experiments in the formal sense of the word. Students learn from firsthand experience in the process of trying to build the projects and make them work. Each project demonstrates several science or math concepts that can be found in most curricula and lists of standards. Each project has been tested in between 10 and 30 classes over the course of four years. I can be confident when I say: the projects work.

You can have great times with your kid while building stuff. Here are some pointers to make the process work:

✳ **Don't take over your kid's project.** If you get so excited about it that you grab it from them to do the next step, you've overstepped your

continued...

mandate. There are safety issues to be sure, but don't let the off chance of a small cut or scrape stand in the way of your youngster's learning to use a new tool or build a great project.

✳ **Don't demand perfection.** Even built crudely, most of these toys will work. Polish comes with practice. The kid's pride in completion is the priority.

✳ **Let kids make mistakes.** Many times a mistake will teach more than will a first-time success.

✳ **Know your role: you are the *assistant*.** If you want to build your own toys, wait until your kid goes to bed. I'm serious: if your kid sees your success to be better than his or her own, the child may be put off from trying another project. But if you can work together with your kid in a way that demonstrates you're helping without taking the lead, you'll have hours of fun together. I find a good technique is to be fiddling with something unrelated nearby. That way I can easily step in and out of the kids' work with advice and help, without having to twiddle my thumbs as they slowly learn how to do something I already know.

The toys here span the technical subjects: physics (including sound, light, mechanics, electricity, and magnetism), chemistry, geology, and biology. Usually several topics can be explored with a single project. The toys are ideal for sparking students' interest in a concept area, and can be used as stepping-stones toward more learning.

Happy assisting!

STOMP ROCKETS, CATAPULTS, AND KALEIDOSCOPES

hOliDAY light CiRCUit

A 9-volt battery will light these tiny bulbs, if you hook them up right.

PARTS

2 film canisters or wood blocks	Weight (nut or bolt)
Baseboard	9-volt battery
½ paint paddle	Battery snap, or two small paper clips
Craft stick	File folders or stiff paper
3 8-inch wires, thin, with insulation	
1–3 holiday lights in a row, cut from a standard string of small holiday lights	

The Basic Concepts

Electricity has to have a complete path in order to travel from one side of a battery to the other. This path is called a circuit. A switch "breaks"—or opens—the circuit and stops the electricity flowing. A battery "pushes" the electricity around the circuit. When the chemical reaction within the battery runs out of chemicals, the battery is dead and can't push anymore.

Build It!

Glue a film canister to the middle of one edge of the baseboard. Cut a paint paddle to be about 9 inches long. Glue a craft stick to one end of the paint paddle.

Glue the other end of the paint paddle to the edge of the baseboard and also to the film canister. Glue the other film canister on the opposite edge of the baseboard, as shown.

Strip the insulation off both ends of three 8-inch wires. Strip both ends of the holiday light wires.

Connect one 8-inch wire to each end of the holiday light wires. One of these wires will go directly to the battery, the other to the craft stick.

Drape a second 8-inch wire over the craft stick and wrap it around once. Tie the weight to this wire near the bottom. Wrap the third 8-inch wire around the paint paddle and make a loop that encompasses the hanging wire. This wire will go directly to the battery. These two wires need to be stripped about 5 inches from one end. When the hanging wire swings, it should contact the loop wire.

Put a battery in the film canister near the paint paddle. Use a 9-volt battery snap if you have one. If not, connect one paper clip to the loop wire and one to the wire coming from the lights. Connect the paper clips to the battery snaps, taking care not to let them touch each other. When you're finished, there should be a single series circuit: from one side of the battery, to the holiday lights, to the swinging wire, to the loop of wire, and back to the battery.

Draw a picture of a snowman (or whatever you'd like) on the file folder or thin cardboard and cut it out. Make a hole in the picture with a screwdriver for each light. Each hole must be big enough to hold the light firmly. Insert the lights, and glue them in place if they do not stay by themselves.

Glue the figure to the front film canister.

Add craft sticks for rigidity if it does not stand up on its own. Swing the weight back and forth. The lights will flash every time the dangling wire touches the loop completing the circuit.

More to Think About and Try

---

* What happens when one light goes out?
* If you put more lights in the circuit, would they be brighter or dimmer?
* How could you make it blink longer?
* How could you make it blink faster?

A Little Background

Wire is the conductor through which the electricity travels in this circuit. Air, on the other hand, is a pretty good insulator. So when the weight is swinging and the wire is not touching the loop, electricity does not travel through the circuit. This is known as an open circuit and is exactly the arrangement in a light switch when you shut off the light.

When the wire holding the weight touches the loop wire, the circuit is complete and electricity can travel through it. The lights glow. This is called a closed circuit.

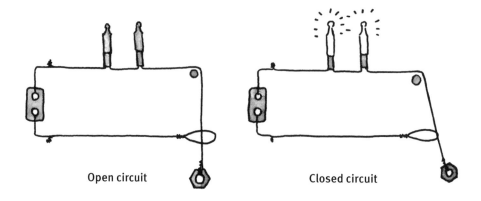

Open circuit   Closed circuit

If you happen to cross the two bare ends of the holiday light wires, the lights will go out but the battery will continue pushing electricity around a circuit. Since there are no lights and just wire in this new circuit, it is smaller, that is, shorter, than the one you had before you touched the wires. This situation is called a short circuit.

The lights that went out when you shorted them had some resistance, which limited the amount of electricity that could flow through them. When the circuit is shorted, this resistance is gone and much more electricity can travel around the circuit. In this project the worst that will happen with this type of short circuit is that the battery will get warm and go dead rapidly. However, if the battery was much bigger and could supply a lot of electricity, this would be a dangerous situation. The wires or other components of the circuit could become hot and perhaps explode. This is why homes have fuses or circuit breakers. Both of these instruments open a circuit that suddenly has too much electricity traveling through it, usually due to a short circuit.

Electric circuits come in two varieties: series and parallel. Try taking one lightbulb in a string of holiday lights out of its socket. The other bulbs should go out. Bulbs in a series circuit act this way. The electricity goes through each bulb, one by one; if you take one out, you have opened the circuit. Bulbs wired in series have to share the total voltage of the circuit. For this reason, you can use these lightbulbs with a 9-volt battery when they were designed to be used with a 120-volt wall outlet. You used only two or three, whereas in their original circuit, there were perhaps 50 bulbs sharing the 120 volts.

You can also wire holiday lights in parallel—try it! Set it up like the drawing on p. 5. Cut two lightbulbs out separately and strip the wires on

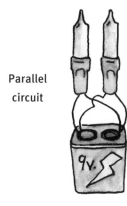

either side of them. Connect one wire from one bulb to one wire from the battery, and then connect the other wire from that bulb to the other battery wire. That bulb should light up. Then connect one wire from the other bulb to one of the connections you just made and the other to the other. Both lights should now glow.

Now try removing one bulb. The other should stay lit. This is because each bulb has its own path in a parallel circuit. Each type of circuit has its advantages. You may notice that the bulbs wired in parallel glow more brightly. This is because they each get the full voltage of the battery. On the other hand, they'll use more electricity and the battery will go dead sooner.

In a series circuit, if you have fewer lights, each will shine brighter. Each additional light adds more resistance, which results in less electricity flowing. To get them to blink faster, you'd need a shorter wire on the pendulum through the loop. A heavier weight would help them to continue blinking longer.

CRANE

Magnets are more useful if you can turn them off and on.

PARTS	
3-inch 1-by-2 wood	Baseboard
6-inch dowel (¼-inch diameter)	6-foot magnet wire (around #30)
Paint paddle	Bolt, screw, or nail (1 inch)
6-inch 2-by-2 wood	2 18-inch wires, thin, with insulation
2 nails, thin (1¼-inch)	Aluminum foil
#6 washer	C battery
String	Paper clips or small nails
Film canister with lid	
TOOLS	
Wire strippers	Sandpaper for stripping magnet wire

The Basic Concepts

Moving electricity creates a magnetic field. If you make electricity run around and around in a coil of wire, you can concentrate the magnetic field and create a strong electromagnet. An electromagnet is much like a permanent one but with an added benefit: you can also turn it off and on at will.

Build It!

Cut a 1-by-2 to be 3 inches long. With a $^{15}\!/_{64}$-inch bit, drill two holes at each end of it. Cut two pieces of ¼-inch dowel, about 4 inches and 2 inches. Hammer them in the two holes so that they stick out of opposite sides.

Drill a $^{15}\!/_{64}$-inch hole near one end of a paint paddle.

With a nail bit, drill a small hole near the other end of the paddle. Drill a $^{19}\!/_{64}$-inch hole near one end of a 6-inch 2-by-2.

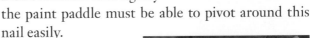

Hammer a nail with a washer through the hole in the paint paddle into the 2-by-2 near the end without the hole. Don't hammer it in tightly— the paint paddle must be able to pivot around this nail easily.

Cut a piece of string a bit longer than the paint paddle.

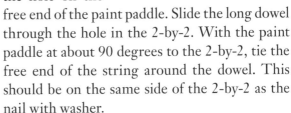

Tie the string to the hole on the free end of the paint paddle. Slide the long dowel through the hole in the 2-by-2. With the paint paddle at about 90 degrees to the 2-by-2, tie the free end of the string around the dowel. This should be on the same side of the 2-by-2 as the nail with washer.

Drill a ¹⁵⁄₆₄-inch hole in a film canister lid. Press it on the dowel so that the string is restricted to a small space between the lid and the 2-by-2.

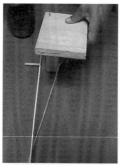

On the table or floor, start a nail into the baseboard near one corner. Turn your 2-by-2 upside down and finish pounding the nail through the baseboard into the end of the 2-by-2.

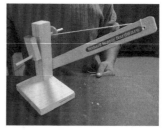

Turn it over and the mechanical part of your crane is finished.

To build the electromagnet, cut about 6 feet of magnet wire. Sand off about 1 inch of insulation (lacquer) at both ends.

Wind the magnet wire around the bolt, leaving both ends sticking out a bit. Twist them to prevent unwinding.

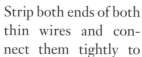

Strip both ends of both thin wires and connect them tightly to the ends of the magnet wires. Keep the two points of connection from touching. This is the electromagnet.

Dangle the electromagnet from the tip of the paint paddle. Tape it on.

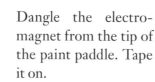

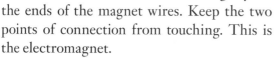

Run the wire down the paint paddle, then off to the side. Glue the film canister down to the base beside the 2-by-2. Fold some aluminum foil onto the end of one wire and stick it into the film canister. Put the battery in the film canister so that it rests on the wad of aluminum foil.

Place some paper clips or small nails on the table. Reel your crane down so that the electromagnet touches the pile of paper clips. To turn it on, connect the stripped end of the free wire to the top of the battery. When you see the paper clips sticking to the electromagnet, reel your crane up.

Pivot the 2-by-2 to swing the crane to the side. When the electromagnet is over the place you want to drop the paper clips, release the wire from the top of the battery and they should fall.

More to Think About and Try

* How is this project different from a real crane?
* How could you tell if a nail or bolt has become permanently magnetized?
* What do you think would happen if you hook up a car battery to the electromagnet you made?
* If you don't use wire with insulation, your electromagnet won't work. Why do you think that is?

A Little Background

Atoms of all elements have magnetic fields associated with them. These fields arise from quantum effects (having to do with electron orbits and spins—very difficult to explain) and are very small for most atoms. Iron atoms, and to a lesser degree cobalt and nickel atoms, have special structures that make a large magnetic field possible. These elements can become the permanent magnets you may find holding up a photo on a refrigerator door.

Electrons are subatomic particles that are less tightly bound to an individual atom than the more massive particles at the atom's center. Electrons may travel from one atom to another, and when they do, that movement is called an electric current. Every electric current creates a magnetic field. In this project you've made an electric current flow many times around a bolt. This "organizes" the magnetic field and results in two distinct poles at either end of the bolt. The bolt also increases the strength of the magnet; if you take it out, the electromagnet will be much weaker.

It is easy to increase the current to your crane, making the magnet stronger: just add more batteries. But if you hook your crane up to a car battery, which can provide enough current to turn an entire car engine, you'll rapidly have an extremely hot coil. The wire will likely melt down at its weakest point. (In addition, car batteries are dangerous. They are filled with acid strong enough to burn you and they sometimes produce hydrogen gas, which can make the battery explode and spray acid all over your face. If you want to increase the current, it is safer to use lantern batteries or line up several D cells than mess with a car battery.)

If your nail or bolt sticks to other iron objects after you switch off the electromagnet, you've transformed it into a permanent magnet. If you used wire with no insulation, when the electricity came to the coil, it would not need to go around and around along the wire. Instead, it could jump sideways from loop to loop until it came to the wire leading back to the battery. Electricity looks for the easiest path and will not go running around loops if there is a faster path—that is, a short circuit. Insulation keeps the current traveling down the wire so that it goes around the coil.

Electromagnets are generally used to move iron or steel objects. Some machines that sort recycled materials use magnets, and cranes such as this model use magnets to transport heavy iron or steel objects. But all materials are magnetic at a much lower level—that is, you can't often move them with magnets. The medical procedure known as magnetic resonance imaging (MRI) is performed by placing a person inside an enormous electromagnet, switching it on and off, and looking at the way the various atoms of the human body respond to the magnetic field.

electriC CAR

A small motor and a small battery will make a small car go fast.

PARTS	
2 craft sticks	2 wires, thin, with insulation
Drinking straw	Aluminum foil
3 film canister lids (or other circles for wheels)	AA battery
	2 paper clips (small)
Bamboo skewer	Wire and paper for flag
Hobby motor, 1.5–3 volts	
TOOLS	
Nail for making axle holes	Wire strippers

The Basic Concepts

The car in this project gets its energy from a battery. The motor will work only if it's connected in a complete circuit to the two sides of the battery. If you reverse the wires, the motor will go in the opposite direction.

Build It!

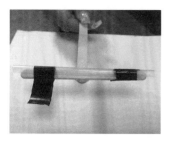

Hot glue the tip of one craft stick to the center of another craft stick in the form of a T. Cut a drinking straw a little bit longer than the craft stick; then tape the straw to the craft stick as shown. It is best to make the straw stick out over both ends so that the wheels will rub on the straw and not the craft stick.

Make a hole in the center of three film canister lids with a small nail. Slide a bamboo skewer inside the drinking straw. Then put one wheel onto each end of the skewer. Cut the excess length, including the dangerous point, off the bamboo skewer.

Hot glue the motor to the end of the craft stick so that the shaft is exactly 90 degrees to the stick.

Press the last wheel onto the motor's shaft. If necessary, add glue to the end of the shaft to secure the film canister lid. Be careful not to let the glue cause the shaft to stick to the motor housing.

Strip the insulation off both ends of two wires. Connect the wires to the motor and wrap the excess wire around the craft stick.

Cut two pieces of aluminum foil and fold them several times into long rectangular shapes. Tape the pieces of aluminum foil tightly to the battery, leaving a bit of foil sticking up on each side.

Hot glue the battery to the top of the craft stick. Connect paper clips to the ends of both of the wires.

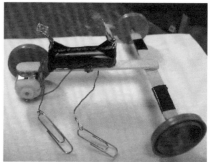

Connect the paper clips to the foil pieces sticking up off the battery. The car should go! Reverse the wires and watch what happens. If you want, make a flag from wire and paper and attach it to the back of the car as shown.

More to Think About and Try

* Where does the car get its energy?
* How can you make the car turn corners?
* How could you make the car go even faster?
* What can you do to make your car change directions?

A Little Background

Batteries store energy. There are two chemical reactions ready and waiting to happen in every battery. One of them creates excess electrons, and the other requires the addition of electrons. If you connect a battery's positive and negative terminals, the reactions begin happening and electrons go racing through the wire from the negative terminal to the positive one. This is electric current.

The wire you use to connect the terminals may get quite hot if you make a direct connection across your battery. The battery will also go dead quickly because all the chemicals are used up quickly in the reactions. To get some work out of the battery, you would need to send the current through something that will make use of the current, such as a motor.

Take apart a motor to see what is inside. You will find little coils of wire and little permanent magnets. When the motor has current running through it, those little coils turn into electromagnets. They then push and pull on the permanent magnets, making the motor turn. The electromagnets are turned off and on at just the right time by tiny brushes touching the shaft of the motor. When the electric current is going through the electromagnets in the opposite direction, they push and pull in the opposite direction and the motor turns in reverse.

By gluing either the front or back wheels at an angle, the car can be made to turn. If you had another motor to control the turn, you could make a remote-controlled car. If you want your motor to go faster, you could put on another battery, but that would also make it heavier. Heavier things generally have more friction, so it may not go faster after all.

electROStatics

Build up a charge, and you will feel the force!

PARTS	
Rubbed Balloon	
Balloon	Pencil
Piece of wool	Aluminum can
Hair	Plastic bottle
Bits of paper	Kite string
Salt	½ CD case
Pepper	
Flying Hydra	
Plastic string (or a very thin plastic bag)	Balloon
Piece of wool	
Small Spark	
Aluminum pie plate	Balloon
Large plastic cup	
Tape Testers	
Two pieces of 5-inch frosted "invisible" tape	"Small Spark" cup-and-plate setup
	Balloon

The Basic Concepts

Electrostatic charge builds up when you rub two insulators together. Conductors carry electricity; insulators usually just hold it. But everything becomes a conductor if you "push" electricity through it hard enough.

A spark is electricity passing through the air, just like lightning.

Opposite electric charges attract, and likes repel, just as with magnetic poles. Charged objects also attract neutral ones. For each activity, you can decide whether it is an example of opposites attracting, likes repelling, or a charged object attracting a neutral object.

Build It!

Rubbed Balloon

Blow up a balloon and rub it with a piece of wool. See what items you can attract to the balloon: hair, bits of paper, salt, pepper, pencils, aluminum cans, plastic bottles, kite string, and so on.

Cover some of the items with half of a CD case and try to attract them to the balloon through the cover. Carefully watch their behavior as you hold the balloon close by.

Flying Hydra

Cut a piece of plastic packing string about 4 inches long. Unwrap it so that it is only one layer. If you can't find this sort of string, you can use a small piece of the thinnest plastic bag you can find. Hold one end down on the table and score the other end with scissors so that it turns ragged with tiny strings. This is the "hydra." Rub it with a piece of wool.

Rub the balloon again and throw the hydra into the air. Put the rubbed spot of the balloon directly under the hydra and it should push the hydra up. Move the balloon around to keep the hydra floating. This activity works well with two people—one rubbing the hydra and throwing it, one rubbing the balloon and floating the hydra.

Small Spark

Hot glue an aluminum pie plate to the top of a plastic cup. Place it away from other objects on the desk.

There are four steps to the process that can be repeated over and over. First, bring the balloon up close or even touching the pie plate. Then, touch the pie plate with a finger to get the first spark.

Remove the finger first, then the balloon. And finally, touch the pie plate again to get the second spark.

After that you can begin all over again. See how many times you can do it.

Tape Testers

Stick one 5-inch piece of "invisible" tape to the table so that it extends over the edge. Stick another directly on top of it, but leave the tail end separate. Mark a T for "top" on the top one.

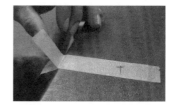

Lift the bottom piece off the desk, and hold one with each hand. Rip them apart rapidly. Bring them back close together and see if they attract each other. They should. They should also attract almost anything you bring

close to them. Try it! These two tape pieces are oppositely charged and can be used to test any object for its electric charge.

Charge up the pie plate by getting the first spark from it. Bring the top tape close to it; it should probably attract. Bring the top tape close to the balloon in the place where you rubbed it; it should probably repel, and it should definitely have the opposite reaction it did with the pie plate. The bottom tape should have the opposite reaction to these two objects.

More to Think About and Try

* How could you get your balloon to make an even bigger shock?
* Can you get a shock through your clothes?
* Can you get a shock if you touch the pie plate with a paper clip or nail?
* Do the tape pieces that you pulled apart attract and repel the same from both sides?

A Little Background

Here are some observations that you should be able to confirm yourself:

* When you rub a balloon with wool, the balloon attracts and is attracted to many things, including the piece of wool you rubbed it with.
* If you also rub a bit of plastic string with wool, it will repel the balloon.

✳ If you bring the rubbed balloon close to the pie tin, insulated on a cup, you can get a small spark upon touching the pie tin.

✳ If you stick two pieces of tape together and then rip them apart, you can see that they'll attract and repel various things. Sometimes they'll both attract something, but you'll never find them both repelling the same thing.

These observations can provide proof of the theory of electrostatics.

This project is about the behavior of charged objects. "Charged" means they hold a net electric charge. Scientists often talk about making or *generating* static charge, but more accurately, they are *separating* the two types of charge. The two types are called positive and negative. Benjamin Franklin came up with these names, and it is good to remember that there is nothing particularly positive or negative about the kinds of charge—they are merely different and opposite. He could have called them black and white or hot and cold.

Before you rubbed the balloon and wool, they were neutral, meaning they contained an equal amount of positive and negative charges. But while you were rubbing, one of the materials pulled harder on the negatives and the other on the positives so that there was a movement of charges, resulting in a net difference in electric charge.

Then—and this is a key point—the charge that moved could not move back to where it came from. It stayed there as a "static" electric charge. That is why this type of electricity is called static electricity. When you touch a highly charged object, such as the pie plate, you can see a spark. This is what you may think of in relation to static electricity, but the spark means charge is actually flowing, as opposed to sitting in one place. Most of the charges in this activity couldn't move because you were using insulators and not conductors. In the pie plate activity, the pie plate is a conductor, and charge is free to move.

The charged balloon exerted force as follows:

✳ A pull on neutral objects (salt, string)
✳ A pull on objects charged the opposite way (wool, one of the tape pieces)
✳ A push on objects charged the same way (rubbed plastic string, the other tape piece)

This is the fundamental law of electric charges. You have heard some of it before: "Opposites attract; likes repel." You don't often hear that charged objects can also attract neutral objects, but this is equally true. The mechanism is called electrical induction.

The tape testers become charged when you rip them apart, one positive and one negative. They'll attract any object with the opposite charge *and* any neutral object. Thus, you can't tell much from attraction. But when you see one repelling another object, you will know it has the same charge as that object. The rubbed balloon usually has the same charge as the top piece of tape. The charged tape pieces generally attract and repel the same on both sides.

A built-up electric charge will always try to flow to the ground or to some large neutral object. You yourself are usually a large neutral object connected to ground (but not if you've been scooting your shoes around on carpet on a dry day or sliding down a plastic slide—then you're highly charged), and if you rub your balloon and then touch it all over with your hands, you can remove the charge.

Try to explain each of the observations you make in terms of the theory described above.

Thanks to Paul Doherty and others at the Exploratorium Teacher Institute for several of these electrostatics ideas.

MAGNETIC SPINNER

It looks like magic, but it's only magnets pushing and pulling on each other.

PARTS	
½ paint paddle	Drinking straw
Baseboard (at least 8 inches by 3 inches, ½-inch thick)	Ring magnet (¾-inch diameter, ³⁄₁₆-inch thick, ¼-inch hole in center)
2 block magnets (1 inch by ¾ inch, ³⁄₁₆-inch thick)	Film canister base (or lid with large divot)
	Color wheel
12-inch dowel (¼-inch diameter)	
TOOLS	
Pencil sharpener	

The Basic Concepts

Magnets can exert force on iron and other magnets without touching them. This is called a magnetic field.

Magnets have two sides called north and south. Like sides push on each other, opposite sides pull on each other, and both sides pull on iron.

When something is supported by magnetic repulsion, there is very little friction. This is the way magnetic levitation trains work.

Build It!

Cut about 4 inches of a paint paddle. Hot glue the paint paddle to the short edge of the baseboard.

Cut two 1-inch pieces of a dowel. Hot glue these pieces, slightly off center, to the rectangular (block) magnets. *Important:* The magnets' faces (opposite the dowels) must push on each other. If they don't (if they attract), take off one dowel and put it on the other side of the magnet; then check it again.

Draw a straight line from the center of the paint paddle to the opposite end of the baseboard.

Put one of the magnets on this line, centered, and mark both sides of it. Glue the magnets down symmetrically as shown above right, each with one edge on the lines you just made. Again, be sure the faces repel each other—the project will not work if they are attracting.

Cut a dowel at least 1 inch longer than your baseboard. Sharpen it to a fine point. Cut 1 inch of a drinking straw. Insert the straw into the ring magnet; then insert the sharpened dowel. The straw should hold the magnet firmly on the dowel.

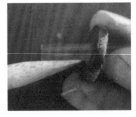

The magnet must slide up and down the dowel but only when you push on it. Put the sharp point of the dowel up against the paint paddle and begin experimenting with the stick to get it to float horizontally. To get the ring magnet in exactly the right spot on the dowel is quite a trick. The correct side of the magnet must be facing toward the paint paddle, and you can determine the correct side only by trying. If you try for a while and it's not working, remove the ring magnet, flip it around, thread it back on, and try again.

Once you have the dowel floating horizontally, mark the spot where the dowel point is touching the paint paddle.

Cut the bottom out of a film canister with a knife or scissors. You may use a film canister lid instead

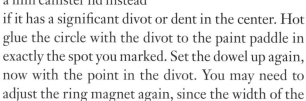

if it has a significant divot or dent in the center. Hot glue the circle with the divot to the paint paddle in exactly the spot you marked. Set the dowel up again, now with the point in the divot. You may need to adjust the ring magnet again, since the width of the film canister plastic forces the dowel farther out.

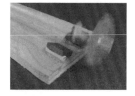

Add a colored circle of paper on the end of the dowel to make the spinning more conspicuous. Alternating colors on this paper will mix when it is spun rapidly.

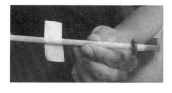

Once the dowel spins stably, stick a piece of tape on it near the magnets. This is to blow on, either directly or through a straw, to keep the dowel spinning.

More to Think About and Try

* How can you make the magnetic spinner float higher?
* What happens if you tip it up vertically?

* Why do you think we had to put a point on the tip of the dowel?
* Why does the spinner stop spinning eventually?

A Little Background

The shaft of the magnetic spinner is not really levitating: the sharpened point is touching the paint paddle and spinning with very little friction. But if one were to try to replace that point of contact with another magnet or array of magnets, it would be impossible to make it levitate. (Don't take my word for it—give it a try!) This is simply the way magnetic fields behave. It can be compared to trying to balance a basketball on a racket ball. In both cases stable equilibrium is not possible.

Magnetic levitation trains and other systems that float on magnetic fields need not have a point of contact, because the magnets they use are electromagnets controlled by computers that use rapid feedback circuits to maintain balance. You can balance a basketball on a racket ball if you are holding the racket ball and changing its position fast enough to stay under the basketball.

If a magnet had only one pole, it would be called a magnetic monopole and have very different properties. No one has ever discovered such a magnet, though, despite decades of searching. All known magnets, from atoms to stars, have a north pole and a south pole. The names "North" and "South" are arbitrary—the important thing to understand is that the two poles are fundamentally different. The only way to determine which pole you are dealing with is to expose it to a known pole of the same type and witness it repelling. If it attracts a known pole, you may have the opposite pole of a magnet or you may have a bit of iron. If you have two identical objects that attract each other from all sides (not repelling at all), it is impossible to know which one is the magnet without bringing in another magnet.

Stronger magnets will make the spinner float higher. If you tip it toward the vertical, it should work until it falls over. If you stick the shaft in a cup and put magnets all around the rim, it will work fine vertically.

The point on the tip of the stick minimizes friction as it spins. There is still some friction, though, which is why it always stops eventually.

Thanks to Tien Huynh-Dinh of the Exploratorium Teacher Institute for proving that even normal humans can make magnetic levitation devices.

SOleNOiD AND SPeAKeR

Electromagnetism works for us every day.

PARTS	
Solenoid	
6-foot magnet wire (#30 or a bit larger)	C or D battery
Drinking straw	Paper clips or small nails to pick up
Aluminum foil	Nail, large
Speaker	
40-foot magnet wire (#30 or a bit larger)	2 magnets (round works well)
3-inch PVC tube (½-inch diameter, to make wire coil)	Paint paddle
	2 paper fasteners (brads)
Paper cup with raised bottom	Rubber band (medium)
Mono plug	
TOOLS	
Sandpaper, small bits	Amplifier (optional)
Radio	

The Basic Concepts

A solenoid is an electromagnet with a hole in the center. When connected, it will suck iron objects into the hole.

Every common speaker has a coil and a magnet. The coil becomes an electromagnet when electricity passes through it. The two magnets then push and pull on each other to make a vibration, which is the sound you hear.

The cup in this speaker works like the diaphragm in a normal speaker: it takes a small vibration from the coil and magnet, and transfers it to the air so that a listener can hear it better.

Build It!

Solenoid

Cut at least 6 inches of magnet wire (the longer it is, the stronger the solenoid will be). Use sandpaper to strip the varnish insulation from both ends of the wire. Leaving a tail of about 4 inches, wrap the wire around the straw near the end.

Leave a 4-inch tail on the other end as well. Twist the two wire ends together so that the coil stays together.

Fold two pieces of aluminum foil around the two stripped ends so that the wire can make better contact with the battery—to be added next. Tape the shorter end tightly onto one end of the battery.

Tape the battery onto the straw

just above the coil. The other end of the wire should just reach to the other end of the battery. This is the switch: when it touches the battery, the solenoid will be on.

Unbend one side of a paper clip and "feed" it into the end of the straw while pinching the aluminum foil to the battery. The paper clip should be sucked quickly into the straw and held even when you turn it upside down. The same should happen with a small nail. When you release the battery, the objects should drop out.

Wrap tape around a larger nail until it wedges snugly when inserted into the end of the straw. This is now an electromagnet. You can pick up paper clips, nails, or other small iron objects. When you disconnect the wire from the battery, they should drop off.

Speaker

Cut 40 feet of magnet wire and wind it around the PVC tube to form a tight coil. Leave at least 1 foot on each of the ends sticking out. Remove the wire from the tube and wrap the ends around the coil so that it holds its shape.

Hot glue the coil securely to the bottom of the paper cup. Sand the varnish insulation off the tips of both ends of the coil.

Take the plastic sheath off a mono plug. You can thread it on the wires to be screwed back on when the connection is made, or just discard it. Connect one end of the wire to each of the terminals of the plug. Note that each of the terminals is connected to one of the two segments of the plug, which are separated by a black band of insulation. The wires can't be touching each other where they have been stripped, nor can the terminals touch. Tape each one separately to avoid a short circuit.

This is the coil and the diaphragm for your speaker. The next step will involve adding the magnet. Glue a magnet onto a paint paddle near the end but not flush. A magnet that fits inside the coil will work best, but any magnet will do.

Poke paper fasteners into either side of the cup near the bottom. Bend them over inside the cup. Stretch the rubber band over the base of the cup and loop one end of it around the heads of each fastener.

Lift the rubber band and slide the paint paddle with magnet under it. The rubber band should hold the magnet near to or touching the coil.

Turn a radio up loud and plug the speaker in. You should be able to hear the radio if you put your ear close to the cup. If you make the coil and magnet fit together very well, you may be able to hear it across the room.

If you have a small amplifier, plug the speaker into its input jack. Now you have a microphone. Speak into the cup, and someone else will hear your voice coming from the amplifier.

More to Think About and Try

* Will the solenoid work if you "feed" a toothpick into it instead of a paper clip or nail?
* How could you make the speaker louder?
* What happens if the magnet is too far away from the coil of wire?
* How is your speaker different from a real one?

A Little Background

You can make a simpler electromagnet with just a nail or bolt wrapped with a bit of wire. The solenoid is more interesting because you can see that the magnetic field is strongest in the center of the coil. When you put a nail in the center, the iron atoms of that nail become magnetically aligned and the nail becomes a magnet. If you put in something that is not attracted to a magnet, like a toothpick, nothing will happen.

Trace the sound from an announcer's voice in the radio studio to the speaker you just made. The announcer's vocal chords vibrate when she pushes air past them. This vibration pushes on air, and sound waves are set up, moving out in all directions from her mouth and vocal chords. Some of these sound waves hit the microphone in front of her. The function of a microphone is to turn sound waves into electric impulses, called a signal. This signal then gets sent to the radio station's transmitter and antenna, where it is converted into radio waves. All the information from the original sound is contained in these radio waves, which get broadcast out in all directions.

If some of these radio waves make it to your radio before they lose their energy, your radio will receive them, convert that information back into an electric signal, amplify it, and send it to the speaker. The function of a speaker is exactly opposite that of a microphone: to turn electric impulses into sound waves. Speakers do this by means of two magnets pulling and pushing on each other. One is an electromagnet, whose strength and direction of magnetism depend on the electric signal that the radio is giving it. All the information from the original sound is contained in that signal, so the electromagnet pulls and pushes on the permanent magnet to create the same vibration that the microphone originally received.

Either the coil or the permanent magnet is connected to the diaphragm of the speaker. When the diaphragm starts vibrating, it pushes on the air and sends out a sound wave. If that sound wave makes it to your ear, you can hear what the announcer is saying.

Speakers can be made louder by amplifying the signal sent to them, by increasing the size of the coil or the permanent magnet, or by making them of higher quality, with less distance between the magnet and coil. The best speakers are still very similar to the one you made, but are constructed so that the coil and magnet are extremely close together. If they are too far apart, the magnetic field decreases in strength and they cannot push and pull as hard on each other. The shapes of the box and diaphragm also are crucial in determining the final sound of a speaker.

ChiRPiNG biRD AND CUiCA

A traditional toy from China and a musical instrument from Brazil will help to explain earthquakes.

PARTS	
Chirping Bird	
File folder or stiff paper	2 straight pins
Drinking straw	String
Bamboo skewer	12-inch dowel (¼-inch diameter)
Fender washer (into which the glue stick tightly fits)*	
Cuica	
Large nail to make hole	Water
Clear plastic cup	Paper towel
String	Pinch of sand (for demonstration
Small nail or toothpick (to tie string onto)	of vibration)
TOOLS	
Chirping Bird	
Stapler with staples	Hole punch

* It is also possible, though a bit trickier, to use a bottle cap, smashed and sanded, in place of the fender washer.

The Basic Concepts

Sound is created when vibration occurs. In the chirping bird experiment, the pin does not slide smoothly on the fender washer—both rub together in a slip/stick motion. In the cuica, the paper moves on the string in the same way. This slip/stick motion is also what produces sound when a bow moves across a stringed instrument. And earthquakes occur when the Earth's tectonic plates, which have been sticking together and building up pressure, suddenly slip.

The volume of a given sound depends on various factors, including how large the object vibrating is and how it makes contact with the air around it.

Build It!

Chirping Bird

Cut a file folder in half. Fold one piece of the file folder in half. Follow the template on the next page to draw the head and wings of the bird, or draw a bird of your own design. Make sure the long side is on the folded edge. The head needs to be big enough for an eyehole. Cut out the shape through both sides of the folder, leaving the folded edge intact.

On the other half of the file folder, draw and cut the tail of the bird. Fold the ends back in opposite directions.

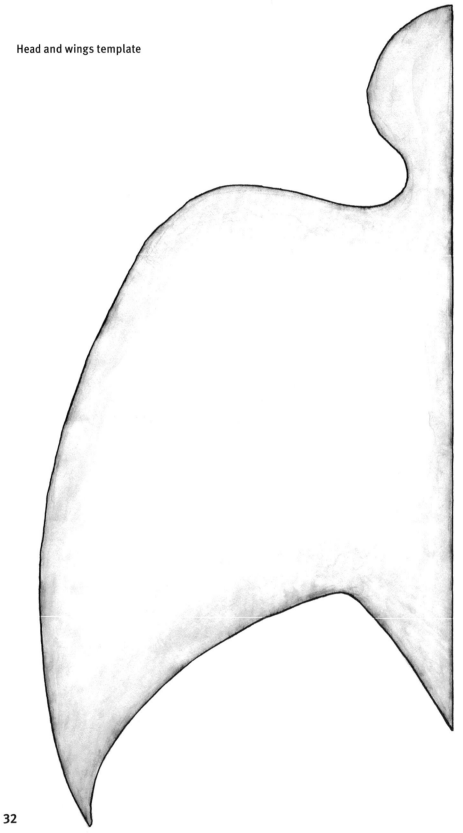

Tail template

Cut the drinking straw so it is a little bit longer than the body of the bird. Insert the bamboo skewer through the straw. Put the straw in the middle of the bird.

Fold the body around the straw and staple it several times so that it

grips the straw tightly but does not stop the skewer from spinning. Hot glue the back end of the bamboo skewer in the center of the tail.

Cut a short piece of hot glue stick. Drill a hole in the piece of glue stick with a large nail. Insert the sharp end of the bamboo skewer into the piece of the hot glue stick. Then, push the piece of hot glue stick through the hole

of the #10 fender washer. Hot glue a straight pin onto the head of the bird so that it extends out in front of the head. The pin must touch the washer, or the bird will not work.

Make a hole on the bird's head with the hole punch. Cut 18 inches of string. Thread one end of the string through the hole and tie it securely.

Cut at least 6 inches of a dowel. Tie the string firmly to the dowel. To operate the bird, spin it in circles and listen for the chirping noise. To trou-

bleshoot, make sure that the tip of the pin is dragging along the washer and that the tail-skewer-washer piece is free to spin. You may also add another pin, opposite to the first.

Cuica

Make a hole with a nail in the center of the base of a clear plastic cup. Cut a piece of string 2 to 3 feet long and pass it through the hole.

Tie the string to the nail on the inside of the cup. The nail will hold the string tightly inside the cup.

Wet a piece of paper towel. Holding the cup with one hand, gently squeeze the string with the wet paper towel and pull the towel down the string. It should make an interesting sound. Drop a pinch of sand into the cuica and watch it dance while you stroke the string.

More to Think About and Try

* How does the bird make noise?
* How could you make the bird louder?
* What would happen if you made a very small tail?
* What do you think would happen if you made the cuica out of a big drum?

A Little Background

The chirping bird and cuica make sound in a very distinct way. The slip/stick motion of the pin tip scratching along the washer is very similar to that of the wet paper towel sliding on the cuica string, chalk screeching on a chalkboard, a violin bow on violin strings, and tectonic plates moving beside each other. There is a period of no motion as tension builds up, then a period of great motion as the two items move from a high-energy state to a low-energy state, then a return to no motion and the slow buildup of tension. With earthquakes, one cycle takes years, decades, or millennia. With a violin, the process happens many times per second.

In both the bird and cuica, the "sounding board" principle is important. On the cuica, try holding the string alone and pulling down on the wet paper. The sound is there, but it is much less intense. The cup helps to connect the vibration from the string to the air. It touches and pushes on more air than does the string alone, and it sends out sound waves with much more energy than just a vibrating string. This is one reason behind the big box of a guitar, and the reason real cuicas (very loud!) are as large as 5-gallon pails. A chirping bird made with a large body may be louder because the body of the bird is the sounding board for the tiny vibrating pin.

The bird may also be louder if it's made with two pins. If you make the tail very small, not much air pushes on it as it flies, so it may not have enough force to spin the washer around. A big tail comes in contact with more air and gives plenty of force to make the pin slide on the washer.

Thanks to an anonymous street vendor in Zhongguancun, China, for the fine Chirping Bird idea. Thanks to the Math and Science Across Culture focus group of teachers at the Exploratorium for the Cuica idea.

MUSiCA:

SAXOPhONE, hARMONiCA, GuiTAR, buII ROARER, OboE, AND SuckER

There is more than one way to make music.

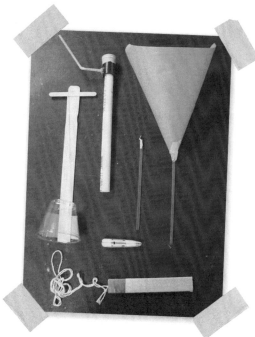

PARTS	
Saxophone	
10-inch PVC tube (½-inch diameter)	Rubber band
Film canister	Drinking straw
Latex glove	
Harmonica	
Clothespin	Rubber band (fat)
Guitar	
Paint paddle	Rubber band (skinny)
Clear plastic cup	Craft stick
Nail (to make hole and to hold rubber band inside cup)	
Bull Roarer	
Paint paddle	Strong string
Oboe	
Drinking straw	Colored paper

PARTS *Continued*	
Sucker	
Paper, any kind	Drinking straw
TOOLS	
Saxophone	
PVC cutter (or hacksaw)	Small drill bit (the same size as drinking straw)
$^{13}/_{16}$-inch paddle bit	

The Basic Concepts

Sound comes from vibrations. The vibrations push on air and make sound waves that travel through the air to your ear. The frequency of a sound vibration is called pitch. The pitch of an instrument is related to its size: large things generally have lower pitch, small things higher pitch. The amplitude of a sound vibration is called volume. The higher the amplitude of vibration, the louder it is.

Build It!

Saxophone

Cut around 10 inches of PVC tube (almost any length works). Make a hole on the side of the film canister. The size of the hole should be exactly the size of the straw.

Use the $^{13}/_{16}$-inch paddle bit *without the drill* to make a hole in the bottom of the film canister. (Paddle bits can be dangerous when used in the hand drill.)

Cut a finger off a latex glove. Stretch the finger over the top of the film canister, but do not cover the side hole.

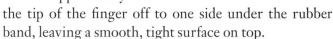

 Secure the finger with a rubber band wrapped many times. Pull the tip of the finger off to one side under the rubber band, leaving a smooth, tight surface on top.

Insert the PVC tube into the ¹³⁄₁₆-inch hole until it contacts the stretched glove. Insert a drinking straw into the side hole. It should extend inside only a tiny bit—not tight against the PVC tube. Glue the straw in.

 Drill holes in the PVC tube with a small bit. You can put nails into the drill platform to help hold the PVC tube and keep it from turning when drilling these holes. Be sure you can reach the holes with your fingers. Blow through the straw to make music.

Harmonica

Take apart the wooden clothespin. Wrap masking tape about six times around the ends of the two wood pieces. The tape must allow a small gap between the wood pieces when you sandwich them together. At one end, the tape should be at the tip of the wood piece. At the other end, there should be a bit of wood sticking out beyond the tape. Make both pieces this way.

Carefully stretch a rubber band around one wood piece. Then, put the other wood piece back-to-back with the first one, sandwiching one length of the rubber band between the wood pieces. Pinching them together, carefully twist the rubber band at one end and loop it back over both wood pieces.

There should be one layer of rubber band between the two clothespin pieces, one on one side and two on the other. Blow through the small hole in the center. To change the sound, pinch the tips that extend from the tape on one side.

Guitar

Hot glue and then tape a full-length paint paddle to the clear plastic cup.

Make a hole with a small nail in the middle of the cup. Poke a rubber band down through the hole.

Thread the nail through the loop in the rubber band inside the cup. Pull up on the rubber band to tighten the nail against the inside of the cup. Glue a craft stick crossways to the other end of the paint paddle. Stretch

the rubber band up and loop it around the craft stick. Wrap it several times around the craft stick to get the right tightness and tone.

Pluck the rubber band to play the guitar. Put the cup to your ear to hear it louder.

Bull Roarer

Cut a paint paddle in half. Glue and/or tape the two halves together. Drill a hole near one end of the paint paddle. Then, tie a string to the paddles. Make the knot very strong, and reinforce with tape if there is any doubt.

Tie a knot on the other end of the string in order to hold it securely. Find an open space and spin it hard. Listen to a roaring sound that starts and stops. Look at the angle of the string as the toy is roaring.

Oboe

Chew on the end of a straw gently to make it flat. Then cut small triangles from each edge near the end, making a sort of dull point. This is the "double reed" of the oboe.

Stick this end in your mouth and blow. If there is no sound, chew it slightly in various directions until a sound comes out.

To make the sound louder, tape together a paper cone for the oboe.

Sucker

Cut a tiny rectangular piece of paper. Stick it on a small piece of tape (any kind). Tape it so that it sticks out over the end of a drinking straw.

 Fold the paper out and then back over the opening. The paper flap should cover the opening if pushed toward it but then spring back a bit when released.

Suck on the straw from the other end and continue to adjust the paper flap until it vibrates and a sound occurs.

More to Think About and Try

* In each instrument, what is vibrating?
* How could you change each instrument's pitch?
* How could you make each instrument louder?
* What happens if you just stretch a rubber band across the paint paddle—without the cup—in the guitar project?

A Little Background

Musical instruments make sound in many different ways, but in each one something is vibrating. In the saxophone the piece of glove is going up and down—feel it with your finger as you blow. This simple instrument is called a saxophone because it sounds like one. In reality, a saxophone has a single reed vibrating against a mouthpiece, not a piece of latex vibrating against a tube.

The harmonica's rubber band stretched between the two halves of the clothespin also vibrates up and down—you can feel it with your tongue. The guitar also has rubber bands vibrating, which then make the cup vibrate. The bull roarer is spinning around, beating the air like a helicopter. In the oboe the sides of the straw vibrate against each other just like a real oboe or bassoon. It is called a double reed mouthpiece. The sucker makes all its noise from that tiny piece of paper banging again and again against the end of the straw.

The pitch of an instrument is its frequency, or how fast the vibration is going: faster is higher pitch, slower is lower. You can easily change the pitch of most of these instruments. You can stretch rubber bands or rubber gloves tighter to raise the pitch. On the saxophone you can also cover the holes in the tube. The air in the tube up to the first hole vibrates together with the glove, so the longer that this tube is, the more air that needs to vibrate and the longer it takes to vibrate back and forth. The bull roarer has a higher pitch if you swing it harder, because it is spinning faster. The oboe and sucker are harder to change. You can change the pitch by cutting the drinking straw or making tiny holes. Since the straw is full of air, different lengths of straw will give different pitches, just as in the saxophone.

To change the volume passing through the instrument is even easier: just do what you do more vigorously. If the amplitude of vibration goes up, the volume increases.

The cup on the guitar vibrates along with the stretched rubber bands. The cup can push more air than the rubber band does, so it sends out more sound waves into the air. The cup serves the same purpose as the box on a guitar. Without it, you'll have a pathetic little sound from your instrument.

Thanks to teachers and staff at the Exploratorium Teacher Institute for the oboe, sucker, harmonica, and saxophone ideas, and to Modesto Tamez for a killer performance on the harmonica.

XYLOPHONE AND MARIMBA

Both wood and metal make interesting sounds when they vibrate.

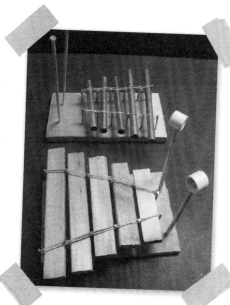

PARTS	
Xylophone or Marimba	
Baseboard (at least 12 inches by 6 inches and at least ⅝-inch thick)	Rubber bands (small)
	2 8-inch dowels (¼-inch diameter)
12 nails (two-headed concrete form type works best)	Cardboard (for feet)
Xylophone	
40-inch steel conduit pipe	2 nuts (¼ inch)
Marimba	
45-inch 1-by-2 wood	2 PVC pipe caps (½-inch diameter)
TOOLS	
Xylophone	
Pipe cutter	
Marimba	
File or sandpaper	

The Basic Concepts

Sound comes from vibrations. If you hear sound, something is vibrating. Sticks of wood and metal vibrate and make sound when you hit them. The frequency, or pitch, of this sound depends on the composition of the material and the length of it. The volume of the sound depends on the amplitude of vibration, which is determined in large part by how hard you hit the material.

Build It!

Xylophone

At one end of the baseboard, make a mark 1 inch in both directions from the two corners.

Lay the ruler so that it starts at one of these marks and angles down toward the center (but not quite at the center) of the other end. Draw a line along the ruler; then draw another one more or less symmetrical with the first, starting at the other mark.

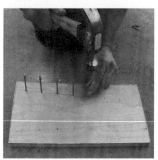

Using the original marks as zeros, mark every 1½ inches down each of the lines until you have six dots. (This is to create five spaces for five pipes. Of course, you can make more if you have the material.) Hammer a nail in at each of the marks.

String two sets of rubber bands along the nails between the two heads.

Mark and cut pipes (from the steel conduit) to the lengths you wish, but make them all different lengths. (Segments of 10, 9, 8, 7, and 6 inches work well.) A pipe cutter works by your tightening it snugly, turning it around the pipe two times, tightening it another one-quarter around, turning around the pipe two more times, and on and on until the circular blade has cut through the conduit. But be careful—if you tighten it too much, it is bad for the blade and impossible to turn the pipe.

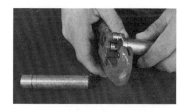

Slide the pipes between the two sets of rubber bands.

Place the longer pipes on the end with the nails farther apart.

To make playing mallets, cut two dowels around 8 inches long. Slightly sharpen one end of each with a pencil sharpener or knife, then thread on a ¼-inch nut until it is tight.

Cut out and glue on small squares of cardboard for feet. These feet have two functions — to avoid scratching the table with any nail tips that protrude through the bottom of the baseboard and to prevent the baseboard from rattling on the table when it is played.

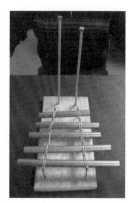

Drill two ¹⁹⁄₆₄-inch holes in one end of the baseboard to hold the playing mallets when not in use.

Marimba

The marimba uses a base with nails in the same manner as the xylophone. The marimba merely replaces the sections of conduit pipe with pieces of wood. The nails on the marimba base must be farther apart, at least

2 inches. The bottom row of rubber bands may be below the double heads of the nails. Cut the 1-by-2 pieces to length with a saw (segments of 11, 10, 9, 8, and 7 inches work well), and then file or sand off the rough spots for a better look and a better sound.

To make marimba mallets, drill a $^{15}/_{64}$-inch hole in two PVC pipe caps. Then, hammer a ¼-inch dowel into each hole.

Use the rounded back of the pipe cap to hit the pieces of wood.

More to Think About and Try

* What happens if you hold a pipe or stick when you hit it?
* How can you make the sound last longer after you strike the pipe or stick?
* Why is the sound different when you hit the pipe or stick with the wooden side of the mallet?
* What happens if one of the pipes or sticks is pressed up against one of the nails?

A Little Background

When you hit something, it tends to start vibrating. Originally the object is deformed; then it springs back to its original position, goes a bit farther because of momentum, stops, starts back the way it came, and on and on. Some materials have little or no elasticity, or spring (water, clay, leather, loose fabric), so when you hit them, they do not vibrate. But most woods and metals do.

A stick of anything may vibrate in several different ways. In one of the primary vibrations, the ends go up and down as the center bulges up and down in the opposite direction. There is a point at about one-quarter of the length of the stick from each end that hardly moves at all as the ends and center vibrate up and down. This place is called a "node of motion," and this is where you want to hold the stick if you are looking to sustain its vibrations. The closer to a node you can support the stick, the longer it will vibrate. The V pattern of the nails on the board is an attempt to support the pipes and sticks more or less at that quarter-length point.

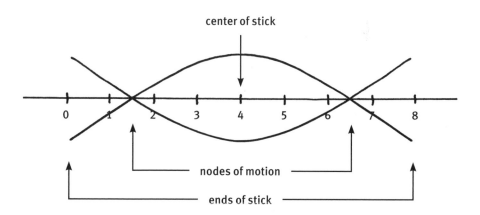

An exaggerated drawing of a vibrating stick in its two positions of "maximum deformation"—that is, the maximum that the stick is able to move when bent like this.

If you hold the pipe or stick anywhere else than at the quarter-length point, or if it is touching something else (such as a nail), the vibrations will be dampened (reduced). If you hold it with something elastic though, such as a rubber band, the stick will be free to vibrate. Thus, you don't need to find the precise node in this project because you are supporting the pipes and sticks with rubber bands.

The material used to hit these instruments also helps determine what kind of vibration will arise and what sound will come out. You can try hitting your xylophone or marimba with many different materials and thinking about why the sounds are different. Using harder objects to hit with will start vibrations faster; softer ones will start vibrations gradually.

KAleiDoScope

If you give it the right mirrors, light will just keep bouncing.

PARTS	
3 plastic mirrors (1 inch by 4 inch)	2 washers ($^5/_{16}$ inch)
2-inch 1-by-2 wood	5-inch clear, flexible tubing ($^5/_{16}$-inch inner diameter, $^1/_2$-inch outer diameter)
10-inch dowel ($^5/_{16}$-inch diameter, for glitter rod, spinner rod, and plugs in tubing)	
	Large cup to trace for circle
Binder clip (large)	White paper
Glitter	Pushpin
Food coloring (or liquid watercolor)	Clear marble

The Basic Concepts

Light reflects from almost everything. When the light that reflects off something enters your eye, you see that thing. Mirrors reflect differently from most things: they reflect at only one angle. Water and glass reflect, too, but not as well as a mirror. Light can reflect from mirrors many times, each time losing a bit of its intensity.

Build It!

Cut a small piece of duct tape and lay it sticky side up on the table. Put one mirror in the center of the duct tape.

 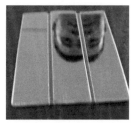

Attach the other two mirrors to the tape on either side of the first mirror, but leave some space between them. Cut off any tape that sticks out around the edges.

Fold the mirrors into a triangle and tape them together, mirrored side in.

Cut about 2 inches of 1-by-2 wood. Glue it on one of the mirrors, close to the end.

Cut two pieces of a ⁵⁄₁₆-inch dowel about 4 inches long. Glue one on between the mirrors and the wood piece so that it sticks out past the end of the mirrors.

Glue a binder clip onto the front of the piece of 1-by-2 wood. The opening of the binder clip should be exactly in the center of the opening of the kaleidoscope.

Put a ⁵⁄₁₆-inch washer onto the second dowel about an inch from the end. Put hot glue on the short end and dip the dowel in some glitter.

Cut two pieces of a ⁵⁄₁₆-inch dowel about 1 inch long. Insert one of the dowels into one end of the tubing. Glue it well.

Put some glitter and a bit of food coloring inside the tube. Then fill the tube with water.

Put the other piece of dowel in the other end of the tube and seal it with hot glue.

Try not to capture any air, but a small bubble inside is OK.

Draw a circle on a piece of paper and cut it out. Decorate it however you want.

Glue a washer to the center of the circle. Insert a pushpin in the center of the circle.

Push the pin into the end of the dowel sticking out beyond the mirrors. The decorated side should be toward the mirrors.

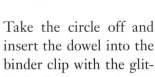

Now it's time to view your kaleidoscope. Slowly spin the colored circle and see the patterns by looking through the other end of the kaleidoscope.

Take the circle off and insert the dowel into the binder clip with the glittered end up. Spin it slowly as you view it. Then, take the dowel out and insert the glitter tube into the binder clip. Turn the kaleidoscope over and over and watch the glitter fall

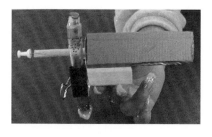

through the water past the opening in the mirrors.

Take the tube out and put a marble at the opening and view it, or instead of a marble, look at anything you want: your finger, your friend, a tree, and so on. The more light that gets into the kaleidoscope, the better it works; so look toward a window or go outside—*but don't look at the sun!*

More to Think About and Try

✳ When you put the marble in the end and look through the kaleido-scope, how many marbles can you see altogether?
✳ What do you think would happen if you put four mirrors together into a kaleidoscope?
✳ What do you think would happen if you used the kaleidoscope at night?
✳ What do you see if you don't put anything at the end of the kaleido-scope but instead rotate the whole thing as you look through it.

A Little Background

Some things give off light: the sun and stars, candles and other flames, lightbulbs, and glowing things. If something gives off its own light, you see it when some of its light enters your eye.

Most things do not give off their own light. You can see these things because they reflect light that is given off by other things. Most things reflect light in many directions. A whole crowd of people can see a rock star on stage because light given off by the spotlights is reflecting off the singer into each of their eyes.

Mirrors are different. They reflect light at only one angle. The angle of reflection happens to be the same as the angle of incidence, that is, the angle the light came in at.

When you look at a mirror, at any given spot on that mirror you'll see one thing. The light coming from that thing (either given off or reflected by it) hit the mirror, bounced off at the same angle as it hit, and then went into your eye.

If you have two or more mirrors, some light may hit one, reflect to the other, and continue to go back and forth. If that light then gets into your eye, you can see the object that reflected or gave off that light. Since light comes off things at all different angles, many different bits of light can take various paths back and forth between the mirrors and then get into your eye. This is how you can see multiple images of the same object.

Each time light reflects off a mirror, it loses a bit of intensity. That's why the images that result from fewer reflections tend to be brighter, while the images that result from many reflections tend to be dimmer. Thus the images seen near the center of the kaleidoscope tend to be crisp, and those seen farther out are not as clear.

How many images you can see depends on the angle between the mirrors, how many mirrors you have, where you put your eye, and where you put the object you are viewing. For each image that you see, you can try to work out which mirror or mirrors the light has bounced off.

thAUMAtROpe

Your eye and brain are just slow enough to see several things at once.

PARTS
Paint paddle
Baseboard
2 craft sticks
Cardboard (thin)
White paper
Rubber bands (medium)
TOOLS
Stapler with staples

The Basic Concepts

Your eye has limits to how fast it can see two distinct pictures. When pictures are moving through the same area too fast, they get "mixed" in your eye. Movies and video screens use this concept. A movie is actually a lot of nonmoving images flashing quickly across the screen. Human eyes can't distinguish the individual images fast enough, so it looks like everything is moving smoothly.

Build It!

Cut a paint paddle in half. Hot glue each half to one end of the baseboard on the same side. Hot glue craft sticks in triangles for braces.

Cut a piece of cardboard that will fit between the two vertical paint paddle pieces. Cut white paper pieces of the same size and glue them to the cardboard on either side.

Slip a rubber band around the resulting sandwich. Move the rubber band exactly to the center and staple it in place. The staple may straddle the rubber band, or it may penetrate it, as shown here.

Draw one half of a picture (such as a face) on one side of cardboard. Flip the piece vertically and draw the other half of the picture (such as a head). Do this carefully, flipping it back and forth in the same way that it will flip on its stand, to be sure it will look right. Draw two halves of a picture that will roughly fit together well; it is hard to make a very precise fit.

Stretch the rubber band from one paint paddle to the other. Twist the two-sided picture over and check them both again. Both pictures should be right-side up as you look at them.

Wind the cardboard up and let it go. If the two halves don't fit together

well, you may have to make another try at
the drawing. You can make several cardboard pieces with different pictures to use
on your base.

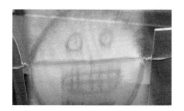

More to Think About and Try

* What would happen if you had three or four sides to the
  thaumatrope?
* Do you think the thaumatrope would work better with a bright light
  or a dim light?
* How could you see the picture on the thaumatrope upside down?
* Why do you think we used small rubber bands on the thaumatrope?

A Little Background

Television programs and movies consist of images flashed on the screen 60
to 72 times per second. In the early days of movies, the images were flashed
much less often, giving a flickering effect. ("Let's go see a flick!") The reason video images appear to move is that your eyes have a limit as to how
fast they can resolve and distinguish flashing images. Flashing images in a
film present motion in small increments. Your eye-brain system puts these
images back together into realistic looking motion.

In the thaumatrope, you see the two images from opposite sides of the
paper at the same time because the cardboard is rotating so fast. If you look
at the back side, the images are upside down. If you put a large rubber band
on, the cardboard rotates even faster. If it turns too fast, the drawings present themselves for too short a time and are less clear. If there were several
sides instead of just two, you might be able to make a real movie, but there
are several factors making this difficult. The images have to be exactly in
the same spot when they come around, and there has to be a moment of
relative darkness between the pictures or the eye-brain system will blur
them. In the two-sided thaumatrope, this moment of darkness happens as
the edge of the cardboard swings by.

bAlANCiNg ACtS

**Watch your center of mass,
or you'll fall over.**

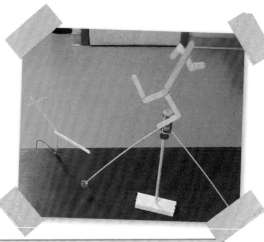

PARTS	
Dancer on a Table	
Craft sticks	Nut (⅜ inch or larger)
Baling wire	
Dancer on a Tack	
Small baseboard	Cork
8-inch dowel (¼-inch diameter)	2 bamboo skewers
Penny	2 nuts (⅜ inch or larger)
Craft sticks	Tack

The Basic Concepts

Everything has a point called its center of gravity, or center of mass. You can think of all the mass of the object concentrated there. An object standing on the ground will balance only if its center of mass is directly above a point that is within the boundaries of its support points. For example, if you lean too far forward, you'll fall over unless you move a foot or hand underneath you.

An object hanging will fall and/or rotate until its support point is directly above its center of mass. For example, if you hang from your hands you'll hang straight down, but if you raise your legs out in front of you, your torso will swing back a bit.

Build It!

Dancer on the Table

Construct a small figure, as shown, with craft sticks and hot glue.

Cut about 12 inches of baling wire. Wrap about 1 inch of the wire around the tip of one of the figure's legs. Then connect a nut or something heavy to the other end of the wire. Bend the wire in a curve such that the craft figure stands up by itself. It can stand on either leg if you bend the wire correctly.

Dancer on a Tack

First, drill a ¹⁵/₆₄-inch hole into the baseboard. Cut a piece of ¼-inch dowel about 8 inches long. Hammer it into the hole. If it is not tight, hot glue it.

Glue a penny flat on the tip of the dowel, with the Lincoln Memorial faceup.

Make a figure—any shape, but not too heavy— with craft sticks and hot glue. On the left is one example.

Use a nail as a drill bit and make two holes in opposite sides of a cork. The holes should be angled upward, so that when you insert the sharp ends of two bamboo skewers into the holes they angle upward, as shown.

Glue nuts to the unsharpened ends of the bamboo skewers. Glue the cork to the lower most stick on your figure.

Glue a tack to the bottom of the cork so that the point is sticking out.

Balance the figure by the tip of the tack pin on the penny. Give it a spin. If it tips too much, glue more weight on the ends of the skewers.

More to Think About and Try

* If your Dancer on the Table doesn't balance right, what can you do to change it?
* If a larger kid and a smaller kid use a seesaw, who should sit closer to the center?
* Why is it harder to walk on high heels than on regular shoes?
* Why would you want to carry two buckets half full of water instead of one bucket full of water?

A Little Background

These projects are about optical illusions as well as center of mass. Since the nuts are small and the figures are large, it looks as if they should fall over. But the nuts are heavy for their size and the figures are light, so it makes sense that the heavy parts will swing to the bottom. If you made the figures from thick wood, they would probably fall over because they would be heavier than the nuts.

Your body has a center of mass, too. While standing, your feet always stay directly under your center of mass. If you try to stand on your hands, you may notice that your hands are not as big as your feet, and you will have to work harder to keep them under your center of mass. To walk in high heels can be hard because your points of support on the ground are so very small. It is easy for your center of gravity to move outside those points of support, at which time you'll stumble or fall. Similarly, if you want a table to be very stable, you'll put the legs far apart. Tall, slender tables with legs close together fall over easily.

If you try to hang from your hands, it will be easy. Gravity just pulls your center of mass directly under the pole you are hanging from. In physics this is called "stable equilibrium," and it occurs whenever you hang something. Think of the exact same system upside down—that is, standing on your hands on a bar. There will still be a point of equilibrium—when your mass is balanced above the point of support on the bar—but it will not be very stable because the bar is so narrow. Instead, you will tend to fall and swing around until you reach stable equilibrium again.

If your dancer on the table is not working, you can bend the wire and weight around so that the center of gravity is below the point of support. A seesaw works because it is balanced on the center pivot. If one kid is a lot heavier, it will not be balanced, so that kid will always be on the ground. But if she moves toward the center, there will be a point where she is balanced with the other kid around the central pivot. Carrying one full bucket of water requires leaning and bending so that you don't fall over. Two buckets of water, one hanging from each hand, are much easier to balance.

CAtAPUlt

Learn physics from very old military science.

PARTS	
32-inch 1-by-2 wood (cut to 9-inch, 11-inch, and 12-inch sections)	3 nails, small
	Bottle cap, film canister, or any small cup (for the bean)
Screw (#8, 1½ inches long)	
2 nuts (#8)	2 rubber bands
2 fender washers (#8)	Cardboard
2 paint paddles	Beans
2 small binder clips	
TOOLS	
Tin snips for cutting cardboard	

The Basic Concepts

There are two important lengths on a lever: between the weight (bean) and the fulcrum (the point around which the lever turns), and between the fulcrum and the force (rubber band). If you change the two lengths, the catapult will shoot differently. There is some combination of these two lengths that will make the weight shoot the farthest.

Triangles are very important in construction. The triangular cardboard supports are crucial to the catapult's stability.

Build It!

Cut three pieces of 1-by-2: 12 inches, 11 inches, and 9 inches. Then, drill a $^{15}/_{64}$-inch hole near the top of the longest piece. Glue the 9-inch piece to the 12-inch one, face-to-face, with ends matching.

Glue the bottom of those two pieces to the middle of the 11-inch 1-by-2.

Insert the screw into the hole at the top of the longest piece. Put on one nut until tight. Put the fender washer outside the nut.

Glue two paint paddles together face-to-face. Clip one binder clip at one end and one at the middle of the paint paddles. Check to be sure the middle binder clip can slide from side to side.

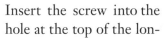

Insert the two handles of the middle binder clip on the screw. Then put on a second washer and then a second nut, finger tight.

Hammer a small nail into the end of the 11-inch (base) 1-by-2 piece on the same end as the binder clip and at the end of the paint paddles.

On the opposite side of the paint paddles (where there is no clip), hot glue a bottle cap.

Tie two rubber bands together; then tie them to the handle of the binder clip at the end of the paint paddle.

Cut two cardboard tri-angles about 12 inches long and 5 inches high. Glue one triangle to each side of the wood base.

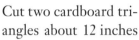

Tie the rubber band to the nail on the end of the base. To operate the catapult, load a bean into the bottle cap, pull the paint paddle down, aim, and let it go.

To improve your shot, slide the center binder clip to a new position and try it again.

More to Think About and Try

* What can you do to make the catapult shoot farther?
* Does it shoot farther with a longer arm on the rubber band side, or a shorter one?
* What is the function of the cardboard? What would happen if you didn't put it on?
* How could you make the catapult shoot straight up?

A Little Background

The catapult is a lever with an adjustable fulcrum. This makes the total length of the force arm and the effort arm a constant: when one gets bigger, the other gets smaller. Another lever is a seesaw. On a seesaw the fulcrum is fixed in the middle of the board, but you can effectively shorten one of the sides by having one person sit closer to the middle.

This is a good project to do a short experiment with. If you mark off the throwing arm every inch and then shoot three times with the fulcrum at each mark, you can average the results for each mark and can find out what the optimal place is for the fulcrum. You can then graph it to see it in a different way.

To make the catapult shoot farther, you can add more rubber bands, shoot a smaller weight, or try to optimize the ratio of lengths between the force and effort arms. The cardboard triangles keep the vertical pieces from bending over when you pull one way or another. To make the catapult shoot up, you just need to rotate the catapult so that the base is vertical.

DANGLING SPINNER

A fraction of a wave is a beautiful thing.

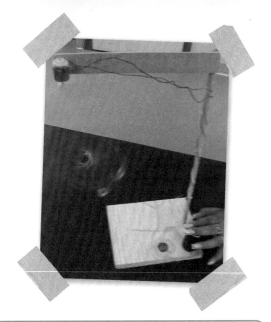

PARTS	
16-inch dowel (5/16-inch diameter)	2 2-foot wires, thin, with insulation
Baseboard	Film canister
Paint paddle	Aluminum foil
Hobby motor, 1.5–3 volts	C battery
Colored string and yarn of different thicknesses	7-inch resistance wire
	Paper clips
Craft sticks	
3 different washers (such as #10, ¼ inch, ⅜ inch)	
TOOLS	
Wire strippers	

The Basic Concepts

A wave on a string can be driven from one end. The motor provides the force and the battery provides the energy. When something is moving fast, your eyes can't follow it. It becomes a blur in the shape of its entire path.

By putting more resistance in the circuit with the motor, a motor will go slower.

Build It!

Cut the dowel to about 16 inches. Drill a ¹⁹⁄₆₄-inch hole in the baseboard. Hammer the dowel into the hole.

Cut the paint paddle at about 10 inches. Hot glue the paint paddle to the top of the dowel. Then hot glue the motor to the tip of the paint paddle.

Tie a string firmly on one of the edges of a craft stick. Tie a washer on the other end of the string. (Start with one string on one end of the stick, for simplicity. You can add another to the other end later.)

Gently drill a hole in the center of the craft stick with a nail bit that is slightly smaller than motor shaft. Insert the shaft of the motor through the hole. If it doesn't hold, add glue to the tip of the motor shaft to hold it in place. You can glue the string onto the stick as shown, or you can use a paper clip to leave open the possibility of exchanging strings (see p. 66).

Strip both ends of the wires. Connect the wires to the terminals of the motor. Run the wires back down the paint paddle and then down the dowel.

Hot glue the film canister to the baseboard near the dowel. This is the battery holder. At the other end of one of the wires tightly fold a piece of aluminum foil. This makes for a better connection for the battery.

Insert the wire end with the aluminum foil in the film canister, all the way to the bottom. Put the battery inside so that it rests on the foil, making a solid connection.

Connect about 6 inches of resistance wire to the other free end of wire. To make the toy spin, press the resistance wire to the top of the battery. The resistance wire will control the speed of the motor depending on where you connect the battery to it. Take out the resistance wire and connect the battery directly to the other wire for maximum speed.

You can create several strings. Instead of gluing them to the craft stick, tie each string to a paper clip then clip it to the craft stick.

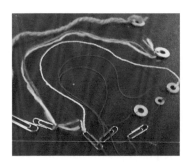

Try it with different sized washers and with no washer.

You can make many different shapes. Other variables you can adjust: speed, string size, washer size, position of paper clip on craft stick, and number of strings hanging.

More to Think About and Try

✳ Which parts of the string go inward, toward the center of the circle when the toy spins, and which move away from the centerline?
✳ What difference does the length make in how the strings spin?
✳ What do you think would happen if you put two batteries on the toy?
✳ What do you think would happen if you tipped the whole thing sideways?

A Little Background

Waves have points of maximum movement and nodes of minimal movement. There is a node at the top of this project where the string attaches to the craft stick on the motor shaft. At the bottom there may be a node if a washer is tied on, or a maximum if there is no washer and the tip of the string flies out to the side as it spins.

Waves produced by this project can be divided into two categories. Waves in multiples of ½ (½, 1, and ³⁄₂) can be produced with a washer tied on the bottom end (creating a node), and waves in odd multiples of ¼ (¼, ¾, and ⁵⁄₄) can be produced with no washer on the end (creating a maximum).

One full wave will include a node to a maximum to a node to another maximum and back to a node.

One maximum surrounded by two nodes make half a wave.

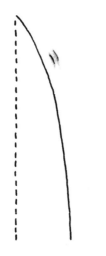 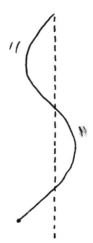

A node and a maximum alone make
a quarter wave.

Try to make various combinations of
these. Here is one and a quarter waves.

Heavier things, such as the washers, tend to stay in toward the center-line of a wave, while lighter things, such as the string, fly out away from the centerline. Different lengths of string give different wave patterns. I have seen students stand up on tables and use 6-foot-long strings to make astonishing kinetic art from their dangling spinners. More batteries give the motor more force to spin. If you can figure out some way of holding the bottom tip of the string but still allowing it to turn, you can tip the whole project on its side. Since both ends are restricted to be nodes in this arrangement, you'll be able to make waves only in multiples of ½.

The resistance wire is like the dimmer switch on a light. It can only resist (or restrict) the amount of electricity going to the motor, not increase it, so it can only make the motor slow down. The more resistance wire the electricity has to go through, the slower the motor goes.

MiNi-bOt

It bounces around a lot, but can you control it?

PARTS	
Baseboard (2 inches by 2 inches and thin)	C or AA battery
Baling wire	6-inch dowel (¼-inch diameter)
2 wires, thin, with insulation	Egg carton
Hobby motor, 1.5–3 volts	Pipe cleaners
2 paper clips	Yarn
Aluminum foil	Plastic eyes
TOOLS	
Wire strippers	

The Basic Concepts

The motor does not make contact with the ground, but it gives force to make the mini-bot move. The piece of glue stick on the motor shaft is not balanced, so when it spins, it sets up a vibration. And as Newton said, for every action there is an equal and opposite reaction. When the glue stick spins to one side, the mini-bot hops to the other side. When the glue stick swings down, the mini-bot hops up, and so on.

Build It!

Drill four holes in the baseboard with a large nail bit, one in each corner. Cut a piece of baling wire, bend it, and force both ends through the holes. Make the wires stay on the board by bending or adding some hot glue.

Strip both ends of both insulated wires. Connect them to the motor. Glue the motor onto the baseboard in any position you think will work.

Connect a paper clip to the free end of both wires. Fold two pieces of aluminum foil. Tape them tightly to the ends of the battery.

Glue the battery to the baseboard.

If you want a neck and head, cut a short piece of dowel. Drill a $^{15}\!/_{64}$-inch hole in the piece of wood at an angle and insert the dowel.

Build a head and face using an egg carton, pipe cleaners, yarn, and plastic eyes.

Cut a piece of hot glue stick. Drill a hole with a small nail bit in the side of the piece of glue stick, *off center.* Press it on the motor shaft.

Connect the paper clips to the bits of aluminum foil and watch it hop. Try to figure out how to control its motion.

More to Think About and Try

* What happens if you attach the motor to the glue stick in exactly the center?
* What can you do to change the direction in which the mini-bot hops?
* What would happen if you put on a very large weight instead of the piece of glue?
* What would happen if you made only three legs?

A Little Background

You may never have seen anything powered in this manner, and the reason is clear: it is nearly impossible to control. Because the motor does not touch the ground or blow on air, the mini-bot is limited to hopping. The direction of each hop is determined by the swing of the piece of glue stick, the weight and balance of its body, the angle of each leg, and its friction with the ground.

If you put a hole right in the center of the glue stick and attach it to the motor shaft—you should try this—the glue stick will spin very smoothly but the mini-bot will not move. It is only when the glue stick is off center that the jumping occurs.

Think about when an adult swings a child around by the hands. The adult cannot be exactly vertical; he or she must lean back in opposition to the direction the child is swinging. On the mini-bot, the body and legs move in opposition to the glue stick.

If you switch the wires on the motor or the battery, the motor will turn in the opposite direction. This will have an impact on the direction the mini-bot hops, though it is not always predicable. The larger the weight spinning on the motor shaft, the harder the motor will have to work to spin it and so the slower it will spin. Different numbers of legs may make the mini-bot act differently, but mini-bots made with no legs—just a flat base—also work. If you make the legs using markers, your mini-bot will scribble you a picture on the table.

Thanks to the students and staff at the Mission Science Workshop in San Francisco for the original idea of locomotion by hop.

RUBBER BAND RACER

The answer to rising gas prices?

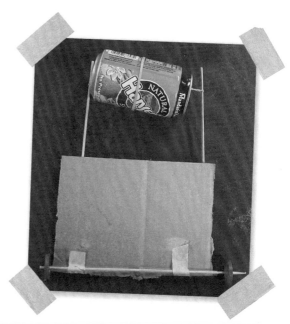

PARTS	
Cardboard (approximately 10 inches by 6 inches)	2 film canister lids (or plastic circles)
	Aluminum soda can
4 bamboo skewers	3 rubber bands (medium)
Drinking straw	

The Basic Concepts

If something that is not moving starts to move, energy is being used and a force exists in the direction of the motion. Energy can be stored by twisting a rubber band. This kind of energy is called "potential energy." When the car is all wound up, it has potential energy.

Energy that is moving is called "kinetic energy." When the car is moving, it has kinetic energy.

Build It!

Cut a piece of cardboard such that its width is less than the length of the bamboo skewers. Slide two bamboo skewers into the corrugation holes of the cardboard.

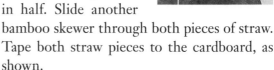

Cut a drinking straw in half. Slide another bamboo skewer through both pieces of straw. Tape both straw pieces to the cardboard, as shown.

Punch or drill holes with nail bit in the center of the film canister lids. Put one on each end of the axle skewer. Glue them if they do not fit tightly, but glue only on the outside so that the glue does not get near the straw or cardboard.

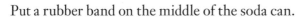

Get a soda can and make a hole with a Phillips screwdriver on top of the can across from the drinking hole. Then make two more holes on the bottom of the soda can.

Put a rubber band on the middle of the soda can.

Get another rubber band and insert one end into the small hole in the top of the soda can. Fish the same end out of the larger hole with the remaining bamboo skewer.

Put one end of the rubber band through the other end. Loop this around one of the bamboo skewers sticking out the front of the cardboard.

Do the same on the other side. Your racer should now look like this.

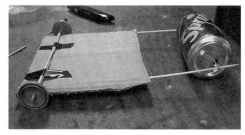

Twist the can many times to wind up the rubber bands then put it on the table and let it run. Turn the car over and see what happens.

More to Think About and Try

* How could you make a rubber band–powered car go even farther?
* Where does this car get its energy?
* Where does a real car get its energy?
* What is the purpose of the rubber band wrapped around the middle of the can?

A Little Background

Rubber (and synthetic rubber) is made from molecules that can stretch or deform a lot before they break apart. When they get deformed, such as when you stretch or twist a rubber band, molecular forces try to reshape them. In this way, you can store energy in rubber. Many materials have this property, but few can stretch as far as rubber without breaking.

In this project you can follow the energy step-by-step. For this project, start at the end and work backward. When the racer stops moving, it has lost all its energy. When it was still moving, it had energy of motion, called kinetic energy. Before it began moving it had no kinetic energy, but since the rubber bands were twisted tightly, they held potential energy. As you wound the rubber bands up, you and the racer had kinetic energy and steadily gave the rubber bands potential energy.

Before you picked up the racer, you had potential energy in your body. This energy was stored in your cells in the form of chemical bonds. This energy came from the food you ate. The food was from either plant or animal. If it was from an animal, it got its energy from a plant, just like you can. The plants in turn got their energy from the sun, through photosynthesis. From one point of view, then, this is a solar-powered car.

If you trace the energy in most things, you can trace it back to the sun. Real cars use gas, which came from plant matter tens of millions of years ago. Those plants also got their energy from the sun. The sun obtains its energy from nuclear reactions—the splitting and forming of the nuclei of dozens of atoms. These atoms in turn got their energy in the formation of the universe.

The rubber band wrapped around the center of the can increased the friction between the car and the ground. This is interesting because usually we try hard to reduce friction so as not to waste energy. But some friction is good. If a car's tires had no friction with the road, the car could not push off and begin to move. When it is time to stop, the car needs as much friction with the road as possible. On an ice-covered road it is impossible to get friction, so cars will continue moving until they hit something.

To make the racer go farther, wind the rubber bands more. If you make a very wide car, you can install longer rubber bands, which can store more energy. You can also install thicker rubber bands, but if the car has too much force, it will not have enough friction with the ground and it will just spin its wheels. You can solve that problem by increasing the weight of the car, which will increase the friction it has with the ground.

VOlADORes De PAPANtIA

("bIRDMeN OF PAPANtIA")

This ancient ritual is actually full of physics.

PARTS	
Baseboard	Bead
24-inch dowel (¼-inch diameter)	12-foot kite string
Toothpick	5 machine screws (¼-inch by 1¼-inches long)
1-by-2 scrap wood piece for drilling holes in cup	
Clear plastic cup (short works well)	Pipe cleaners

The Basic Concepts

By winding the four strings on the dowel, you raise the screws and give them energy. This energy is called "potential energy," or stored energy. The force of gravity pulls the screws down to the ground and makes them and the cup spin. When the screws are spinning and falling, they have energy of motion, or "kinetic energy." Even though gravity pulls only straight down, the toy spins because the strings put a force on the central stick at its edge. This gives a torque that pulls the cup around.

The Voladores de Papantla ("Bird Men of Papantla") is a ritual originating in pre-Columbian times. A small ethnic group called the Totonacas, who lived in the area of Veracruz, Mexico, performed this ritual for the sun god, asking for good harvest and fertility. The post for this experiment can be over 50 feet tall.

⇡ *Voladores de Papantla at the Forum de Barcelona 2004, Marcelo Aurelio—Nocturama Fotoblog, www.arte-redes.com/nocturama*

Build It!

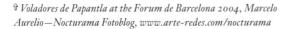

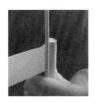
Drill a ¹⁵⁄₆₄-inch hole in the middle of a baseboard, as straight vertically as possible. Hammer the 24-inch dowel into the hole. Tape a toothpick to the top of the dowel such that it sticks up an inch or so.

Clamp a scrap 1-by-2 to extend over the end of the worktable. Drill 4 holes symmetrically in the sides of the cup, near the rim. Make one hole, then the one opposite it; then split the difference on each side. Glue a bead inside the base of the cup in the center.

Cut four strings, each one a few inches longer than the dowel is tall. Make them all exactly the same length. Tape one end of each string to a machine screw. First tape it on so that a

tail extends over the head of the screw. Then double the tail back and tape over that tail. This will keep the string from sliding out from under the tape and will avoid tying any knots.

Insert the free end of each string through one of the holes in the side of the cup, from the outside in. Put the ends together and tie them in a simple knot.

Tape these four strings and the knot to the dowel up near the toothpick. The exact place is not important, as long as the screws can all reach the ground. Put the cup on the top of the dowel with the toothpick sticking into the bead. If one of the screws is a lot longer than the rest, pull its string from inside the cup and tape a bit of it to the dowel.

Attach pipe cleaners to the machine screws as shown to form four fliers. Use an additional machine screw and pipe cleaners to create a "flute-playing priest" atop the cup.

Wind up the fliers. Slowly turn the cup, and they will rise; however, the fliers tend to get tangled up using this method. A better way is to hold the cup steady and twist the dowel and base.

When the fliers are at the top, make sure the toothpick is still in the bead and release the cup.

More to Think About and Try

✳ What would happen if you had only three or two *voladores*?
✳ How could you make the *voladores* spin faster?
✳ What would happen if you had a smaller cup, or a larger central shaft?
✳ What would happen to the other *voladores* if one string broke halfway down?

A Little Background

This may look like a simple toy, but the physics is astonishingly complex. Consider that once you've added your energy and it is all wound up, the only force driving it is the Earth's gravity, which always pulls straight down. Most times gravity leads to a downward acceleration, but the motion of this device is both downward and rotational and at a nearly constant speed. Furthermore, the *voladores* (seen as screws) do not travel straight down as they spin but rather swing out to a certain angle with the central dowel.

You may conduct small experiments to see what difference various factors make. Some possibilities are to make the *voladores* heavier (tape two more screws onto each one), use a thicker central dowel or wrap the dowel with tape or paper to make it thicker, use a larger or smaller cup, tie more or fewer *voladores*, or make the pole longer. In each experiment you will need to do two trials with only one factor changed between them. For example, if you want to see the effect of the weight of the *voladores*, it is best to get two setups with the cups, central dowels, and strings exactly the same; then change just the weight. Once you have two devices with one different variable, let them go and time how long it takes for them to get down, as well as noting any other differences: the angle that the screws swing out to, how long it takes them to get up to speed, what happens when they are down, and so forth. If you have only one setup, you can watch it carefully in one trial, then change one variable, and then watch it carefully as you do it again.

Force that makes something turn is called "torque." The strings exert torque on the central stick in this project, but the stick is fastened down, so the cup ends up turning. The torque results from the strings pulling on the edge, or circumference, of the central stick. If they were fastened directly to the center of the stick, there would be no motion.

The angle that the *voladores* swing out to depends on the speed at which they turn, which depends on the torque of the strings, which depends on the weight of the *voladores*. The rotational speed also depends on the angular momentum, which is determined by the weight and the distance of the weight from the center. So the bigger the screws, the harder they pull; but the bigger the screws, the harder it is to spin them around. Our group found that the weight makes very little difference in how fast the *voladores* spin.

On the other hand, the size of both the central shaft and the cup makes a huge difference. If you make the shaft larger by wrapping it with tape or paper, or just by using a larger cylinder, such as a film canister, the torque alone increases and the *voladores* go spinning down much more rapidly. The same thing happens if you use a smaller cup.

You can wind the toy up halfway, cut one of the strings, and then continue to wind it to the top. When you let go, it works fine until halfway down, when the one *volador* goes flying to its demise. You can then see what happens to the others. They may still live!

Thanks to Gustavo Hernandez for conceiving and developing this project.

AiRPLANeS

Amazing flights are possible with a simple folded paper.

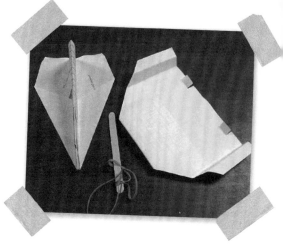

PARTS	
Airplane with Bottom Fold	
Paper	Paper clip
Glider with Flat Bottom	
Paper	Tack
Craft stick	Index cards
Launcher	
Rubber bands (medium)	Craft stick

The Basic Concepts

There are two main factors that will change the way the plane flies: the weight in the front, and the angle of the elevators. Elevators are the horizontal surfaces on the back of a plane that change its angle as it flies. That said, every surface is important; a good plane will be beautiful and perfectly symmetric.

You can have great fun and learn a lot with paper airplanes flown by hand. It is also nice to launch them with rubber bands. Nearly any paper plane can be altered to make it rubber band launched.

Build It!

Airplane with Bottom Fold

Fold the sheet in half the long way. Open it again. Fold the two top corners into the centerline. Then fold the top point over.

Fold the two top corners in again, but leave a flat space on the top. Fold a small triangle up over the two flaps to lock them down.

Fold along the centerline then fold the wings back down. The points at the back of the wings function as the elevators. If your plane goes up too fast, bend them down; if it goes down too fast, bend them up. Folding one up and one down will make the plane turn and possibly corkscrew.

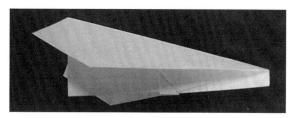

If you want to prepare your plane for the launcher attachment (see p. 85), unfold the long end of the paper clip 90 degrees. Put the paper clip in the center slightly toward the front of the airplane. Poke the open end of the paper clip through the middle crease, so that it sticks out below the airplane.

Hot glue the paper clip in place, closing the fold of the airplane. Cut most of the paper clip off, leaving enough to hook a rubber band.

Glider with Flat Bottom

Fold one of the top corners to the opposite edge and unfold. Repeat with the other top corner, creating intersecting creases.

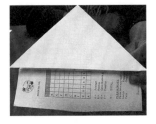

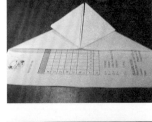

Fold the side creases in, making a pointy top. Fold the bottom tips back up to the top.

Fold the top point down and the two side points up so that they meet. Crease them well. Find the pockets in the top point and insert the two side points into these pockets.

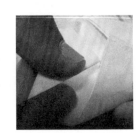

Flip over the airplane. Fold both side edges up a bit to make vertical stabilizers.

Make small cuts on the tail with scissors. Fold the small rectangular section up a bit. These are the elevators.

If you want to prepare your glider for the launcher attachment (see below), make a hole in the craft stick

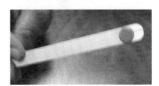

with a tack. Take the tack out, then glue it back in.

Put hot glue on top of the craft stick. Glue it to the bottom of the airplane, exactly in the middle, with the head sticking out just a bit.

Launcher

Connect the two rubber bands together, as shown. Then connect them to the craft stick.

Hook the rubber bands to the tack or the paper clip. Hold the craft stick vertically in front of the plane while pulling the plane back with the other hand. Upon release, drop the craft stick a bit so that the plane does not run into it.

More to Think About and Try

* What do you think would happen if you made a plane out of aluminum foil?
* What do you think would happen if you put more rubber bands on the stick?
* How do you think these airplanes would work on the moon?
* Where does the energy come from to make these airplanes fly?

A Little Background

Aerodynamics and fluid mechanics can get very complicated, but it is quite simple to think about what makes these paper airplanes fly the way they do. When you toss a paper plane, you give it forward motion. Air is the fluid that the plane is flying through—the air will hit the surfaces of the plane just as water would. The angle of the surface will determine the force the air puts on the plane.

If the elevators are sticking up, the air will hit them and push the rear of the plane down. The nose of the plane will then stick up, sending the plane upward. If the elevators are sticking down, the opposite will happen.

A real airplane has at least three control surfaces, one for each of the dimensions in which it is free to travel. On the ground, we are used to traveling in two dimensions: forward/backward and right/left. Airplanes have an additional one: up/down. Whereas a car can turn only right or left, an airplane can turn on each of its three axes:

* Tilting its nose up or down is called "pitch" and is controlled by the elevators.
* Swinging its nose right or left is called "yaw" and is controlled by the rudder, which is part of the vertical surface on the tail of the plane.
* Tilting one wing up and the other down is called "roll" and is controlled by the ailerons, which are on the trailing edge of the two wing tips and which move in opposition to each other—when one goes up, the other goes down.

Some people call the elevators on these paper airplanes "elevons" because they can make the plane roll as well as pitch. An additional complexity is that airplanes actually use ailerons to make turns, "flying around the corner," so to speak. This is different from a boat, which uses the rudder to turn.

Many airplanes have a fourth control surface called the "flaps." Like ailerons, flaps are on the trailing edge of the wings, but normally close by the fuselage (or body) of the airplane. These go up and down together and are used to change the shape of the wing to enable more stable flight at low speeds, usually in preparation for landing.

The materials and construction of a plane are extremely important because the overall weight and the distribution of weight on an airplane will determine whether it will fly. It is possible to make a few airplanes from aluminum foil, especially gliders. If you put too many rubber bands on the stick, the plane will be torn apart as it launches. On the moon there is no air, so the planes would not fly at all but instead behave just as if you had thrown a rock. You provide the energy to make the planes fly, and you get your energy from food, which in turn gets its energy from the sun.

FlYiNg FiSh

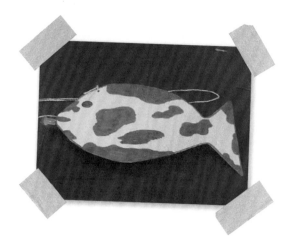

If you want to go forward, throw something back.

PARTS	
File folders or stiff paper	Paper clips
2-liter plastic bottle (for propeller)	Craft stick
Aluminum foil	String
AA battery	Ribbons
Hobby motor, 1.5–3 volts	Long $\frac{5}{16}$-inch dowels (for hanging the fish)
Wires, thin, with insulation	
TOOLS	
Hole punch	Wire strippers

The Basic Concepts

Propellers "throw" air (or any fluid) backward or forward. (Impellers, like in the Tornado project, throw fluid outward.) To make something move forward from rest requires a forward force. But a forward force always comes together with a backward force. This is Newton's third law: for every action there is an equal and opposite reaction.

The energy for making the fish fly comes from the battery. The force comes from the motor and propeller.

Build It!

Draw a fish (or any other long, slender figure) on stiff paper. It should be around 6 to 8 inches long. Cut it out.

Draw lines on a 2-liter bottle *along a slight incline.* This incline provides the twist for the propeller. Cut out a single segment.

Fold two pieces of aluminum foil and tape them tightly to the ends of the battery with black tape.

Strip both wires at both ends and attach them to the motor. Attach paper clips to the other ends of the wires.

Hot glue the motor to the end of a craft stick so that the shaft sticks off the end.

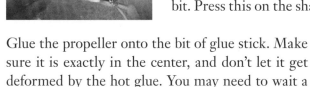

Cut a ½-inch piece of hot glue stick. Drill a hole into the end of the piece with a small nail bit. Press this on the shaft of the motor.

Glue the propeller onto the bit of glue stick. Make sure it is exactly in the center, and don't let it get deformed by the hot glue. You may need to wait a few seconds for the glue to cool down a bit before pressing the propeller on.

Glue the battery onto the craft stick; then glue the craft stick onto the fish, with the propeller at the nose.

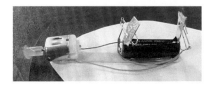

With a hole punch, punch a hole near the top of the fish so that the fish will hang level, that is, without pointing its head too far up or down. Tie a length of string through the hole.

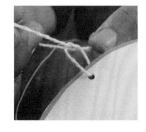

Decorate the fish. You can tie a length of ribbon onto its tail. Hang the fish from the ceiling or another high point, and try to get it to fly around. Launch it straight down the circular path it will follow.

Sometimes it is tricky to get the fish to fly. Here are some troubleshooting steps:

* When the propeller is spinning, it should be blowing air *back* across the fish. Check this by putting your hand by the fish to feel for the air.
* If you can't feel air blowing back, it may be blowing forward. Check this by putting your hand in front of the propeller. If you can feel the air blowing forward, change the wires on the battery to make the motor spin in the other direction.
* If the air does not seem to be blowing forward either, the propeller may not be bent correctly. Both sides should be twisted slightly, just like a real propeller or fan blades. Bend it more if it needs it.
* If it is blowing air backward, but not much, you can tighten your battery connections with tape and twist your wires a bit tighter. Be sure the battery is not dying.
* Once you can feel air blowing back over the fish, you need to launch the fish in the right direction. There is no way to know which way is right. It depends on the direction of the motor but also on the balance of the fish. A few fish will circle in both directions, but one direction is always faster.
* Try launching the fish at different angles and different speeds.
* One other variable to adjust is the length of the string. The fish and string will trace out a cone when flying. The angle that the fish hangs at depends on the size of this cone. Sometimes a different angle will make a fish fly better.

More to Think About and Try

* What makes the fish fly through the air?
* Can you make the fish go in both directions?
* What would happen if you put another battery on the fish?
* Why is it hard to make a real airplane with an electric motor?

A Little Background

Propellers and fans push air. They go around in circles, but they push air perpendicular to the plane of rotation. Most people are more familiar with fans than with airplane propellers, but they are essentially the same. Fan blades are at an angle such that each bit of air they encounter bounces off toward the front or back. If something perfectly flat, such as a craft stick, goes in circles, it does not push much air and thus would not make the fish move.

In this toy the propeller can push air forward away from the fish or back across the fish, depending on which way the motor is turning. Newton said that for every action there is an equal and opposite reaction. In this project, the action is the propeller pushing the air back across the fish; the reaction is the fish being pushed forward through the air.

Gyroscopic effects (strange forces on spinning objects) and center of mass also play into this project. It gets a bit complicated, but for most fish one direction of flight is much more stable than the other direction. The body of the fish is not symmetric; that is, the batteries and motor put nearly all the weight on one side. The orientation of the fish is diagonal as it traces out its circular flight path, and usually the fish is most stable if the battery side is down. But the rotation of the motor-propeller system makes gyroscopic forces that also affect which direction is more stable. This is an example of a complex combination of linear and rotational motion.

The battery provides the energy for this process. The motor takes the energy from the battery and gives force to the propeller. The propeller then gives force to the air (action), which also pushes back on the propeller (reaction) to make the fish move through the air. Thus, the air coming off the propeller pushes the fish forward, much the same way a rocket is pushed forward by the air it is expelling backward through the rocket nozzle.

An electric airplane needs a powerful battery, and that usually means a lot of weight. With cheap hobby motors and normal batteries, you'll never get enough force to make an airplane fly on its own. You can sometimes get a motor and a propeller to fly like a helicopter if you hook up a strong battery, hold the battery, and run thin wires to the motor. Recently some powerful batteries and high-torque motors have been developed that allow for electric remote-controlled airplanes.

heliCOPteRS

What happens when a helicopter's engine quits?

PARTS	
Indoor Helicopter	
File folder or stiff paper	Pennies
Craft stick	
Outdoor Helicopter	
¾-inch PVC tube (½-inch diameter)	2-liter plastic bottle (for wings)
8-inch dowel (¼-inch diameter)	
Outdoor Helicopter Launcher	
2 rubber bands (large)	Craft stick
TOOLS	
Outdoor Helicopter	
PVC cutter (or hacksaw)	
Large pliers (to hold PVC piece while drilling)	

The Basic Concepts

Air is real. You can't see it, but it moves things. The rubber band in this project gives the force that makes the helicopter go up. Gravity gives the force that makes it come back down. The air that it encounters makes it spin around and fall slower. If the blades are bent correctly, the air pushes them to make the helicopter go around.

Build It!

Indoor Helicopter

Cut a helicopter shape out of thick paper or file folder. The simplest shape can be a rectangle with a slit cut down the center. The blades are the pieces on each side of the slit.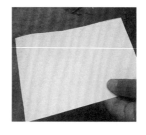

You can make the blades any size you like.

  On the other end of the piece, fold the corners of the rectangle in toward the center. Then glue a craft stick on the center.

 Glue one or two or more pennies to the other end of the craft stick.

Throw it up, and it should spin on the way down.

Outdoor Helicopter

Cut a piece of PVC, about ¾-inch long. With a sharp drill bit, drill a $^{15}\!/_{64}$-inch hole into the center of the PVC while holding it tightly with pliers. You can punch a shallow hole in the PVC with a nail to get the bit started.

Cut about 8 inches of a ¼-inch dowel. Hammer it into the hole in the PVC.

Put some hot glue around the dowel, especially inside the tube. This will keep the dowel from flying out when you launch the helicopter.

Draw slanted lines on a 2-liter bottle. Cut along the lines on the bottle until you have two strips. These will be the blades.

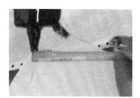

Put hot glue on the dowel. Allow the glue to cool for a few seconds so it does not melt the plastic. Then press the blades onto the glue so that they stick up, in the same direction as the dowel.

Tape around the blades to reinforce the glue. Fold the wings a bit toward the outside and make them symmetric.

Outdoor Helicopter Launcher

Tie two rubber bands together.

Tie the rubber bands to the tip of the craft stick. The launcher is finished.

Launch the helicopter like a slingshot. The hand with the launcher is up in front. The hand pinching the blades is down in back. The rubber band is looped around the end of the tube, pulled toward your body. To launch the helicopter, let go of the blades and move the launcher hand away slightly so that the helicopter does not hit it.

If the helicopter does not spin on its way back down, make sure the blades are symmetric, twisted slightly, and bent opposite each other.

More to Think About and Try

* What do you think would happen if you made the helicopter even heavier at the bottom?
* How could you make the helicopter go up farther?
* What are some differences between this helicopter and a real helicopter?
* What could you change to make the helicopter spin faster?

A Little Background

The helicopter's blades encounter air as it falls. The blades are at an angle, so that each little bit of air that hits them bounces off and pushes them to the side. If you have them bent correctly, each one will be pushed around in the same direction, causing the helicopter to spin. The air also pushes up the blades, causing the helicopter to fall more slowly.

Real helicopters do this in emergencies. If a helicopter's engine fails, the recovery procedure is to begin "autorotation." This simply means that instead of the engine turning the blades, the air flowing past the falling craft will turn the blades. In most cases, this provides enough upward force to slow the descent, allowing the pilot to find a suitable space below for an emergency landing.

This toy requires air to function. If you tried it on the moon, here is what would happen: It would rise to six times the height it rises to on

Earth, because the moon's gravity is six times less than the Earth's. Then it would fall back to the Earth without any spinning at all, because there is no air on the moon.

Let's follow the energy used in this project. You provide the original energy to stretch the rubber band. Your body got this energy by metabolizing the food you ate earlier. When the rubber band is stretched, it holds potential energy. When released, it gives this energy to the helicopter. The helicopter begins accelerating upward. As the helicopter leaves the rubber band, it is traveling as fast as it will go during its flight. The potential energy of the rubber band has been converted into kinetic energy.

The helicopter slows down as it continues upward because gravity is pulling steadily downward on it. It loses kinetic energy as it gains potential energy of height. At its highest point, it stops moving up and has lost all kinetic energy. It holds the maximum potential energy of height it will have. It then starts down.

If the blades spring out properly, they encounter air, which pushes them around. As the helicopter begins rotating, it gains rotational kinetic energy, which uses up some of the potential energy. Some of the helicopter's potential energy is also given to the air, heating it up a bit. Because of these losses, the speed (and kinetic energy) of the helicopter is a bit less on the way down than it was on the way up. Upon impact with the ground, all remaining energy is converted to heat. You won't feel this heat because there is not much energy involved.

hYDRAUliC butteRFly

A crude mechanical model of the graceful insect.

PARTS	
Baseboard	One-piece wooden clothespin
24-inch dowel (¼-inch diameter)	2 feet of clear, flexible tubing (⅛-inch diameter)
2 syringes	
Cardboard	2 craft sticks

The Basic Concepts

Air is compressible (squeezable.) When you squeeze it, it gets smaller. Water does not. Hydraulic systems are often used to give a strong force across a short distance. When driven by a hydraulic pump, the butterfly's body goes up and down as the wings go down and up.

Build It!

Drill three ¹⁵⁄₆₄-inch holes on the baseboard near the edges in a triangular pattern.

Cut the ¼-inch dowel in three pieces: two of them the same size and the third at least an inch shorter than the other two. Hammer the dowels into the holes, with the short one in the middle.

Duct tape one syringe to the top of the middle dowel. Its handle should be about even with the tops of the other dowels.

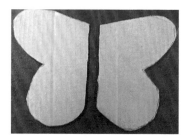

Using the template on the next page or a design of your own, draw one butterfly wing on a piece of cardboard and cut it out. Trace this first wing to create a second, identical wing, and cut it out as well.

Put the wooden clothespin between the straight sides of the two wings. Tape them together as shown, leaving a space that allows the wings to flap up and down.

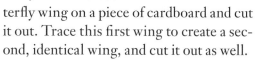

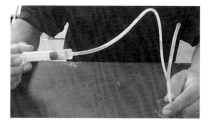

Cut 2 feet of ⅛-inch tubing and press it onto the tip of another syringe.

Over a basin, suck water into the syringe then invert it to expel the air. Do this a few times to get all the air out.

Wing template

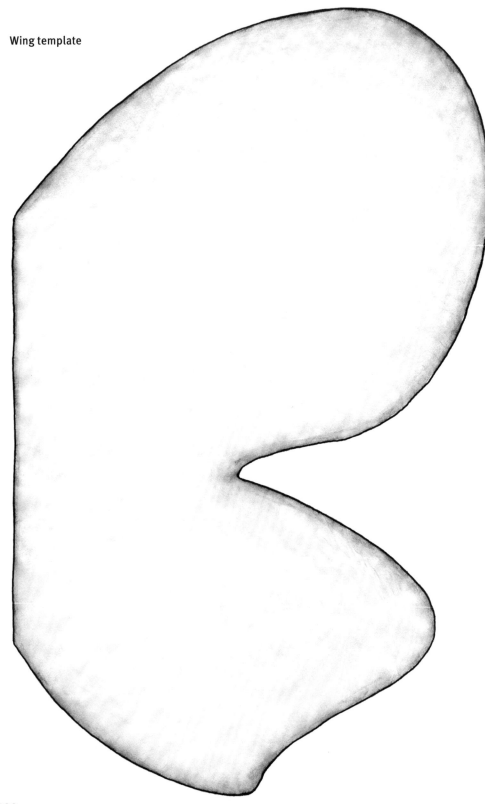

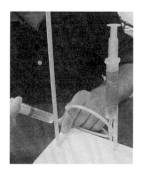

When there is no air in the syringe and tube, connect it to the syringe taped to the dowel. This syringe should be completely closed when you press on the tubing, to avoid air in the system. Compress the free syringe and be sure the piston of the stationary syringe moves up.

Glue craft sticks to the tops of the two side dowels. Hold them steady until the glue is dry.

Put hot glue on top of the stationary syringe and glue on the butterfly's body (the clothespin).

Decorate the butterfly.

Push the syringe up and down to make the butterfly's wings flap.

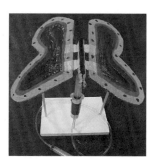

More to Think About and Try

* Why do you think oil is used instead of water in most hydraulic systems?
* What do you think would happen if the tube were very long, perhaps a half-mile long?
* Why do nurses tap on the tubes of syringes and IVs when they are getting ready to give you an injection or set up an IV?
* What happens if there is just air in the syringes?

A Little Background

A simple demonstration will help illuminate this project. Find two identical plastic bottles with lids. Fill one completely up with water—no air bubbles—and leave the other one empty. Tighten the lids and put one in each hand. Now squeeze as hard as you can on the bottles and notice the difference. The bottle full of water will hardly squeeze at all. What squeezing can be done is due to the deformation of the bottle. The other bottle will squeeze quite a bit. It is key to realize that this bottle is not actually empty; it is full of air. When you squeeze air, it gets smaller. When you squeeze water, nothing happens at all. If you were to put the bottle full of water into a giant smashing machine, the bottle would break long before the water would decrease its volume by even 0.01 percent.

This compressibility property reflects the different way molecules behave in liquids and gases. In a gas the molecules are flying freely, bouncing off walls and other molecules. Between these wild flying gas molecules is only space. If you find a way to press on them, such as squeezing them in a closed bottle, you can reduce the amount of space they have. Pneumatic systems (like the ones used in those loud power-wrenches at auto shops) use a gas (usually air) and exploit this cushiony property.

Liquids and solids, on the other hand, have closely packed molecules, bound together much more tightly than gas molecules are. If you push on them, very little happens. You can think about pushing down on a pile of blocks—it doesn't matter how hard you push, nothing much will happen. If you push hard enough on only one end of a pile of blocks, though, the pile will move, and whatever is in front of it will move, too.

In this project you push on one end of a system of liquid. The walls enclosing the liquid all feel the same pressure (force per unit area) as the pressure you give the piston in the syringe. The one "wall" that is free to move—the other piston—then gives way to push your butterfly up. When you decrease pressure by pulling on the piston, the same thing happens in reverse, with the atmosphere pushing the other piston (connected to the butterfly) down into the syringe again.

Hydraulic systems are good at giving a lot of force over a short distance. You find them on construction and manufacturing machines. It is harder to make hydraulic systems move over great distances. Hydraulic motors do exist, making rotating applications available.

Hydraulic systems use oil instead of water because oil doesn't cause metal to rust and because it automatically lubricates the system. If a hydraulic system is very long, many small losses in the tube (such as holes or elasticity) will add up to a greater loss of motion, but the pressure at the point of use will still equal, approximately, the pressure applied.

When getting the air out of your system, you use gravity and buoyancy. Air bubbles will rise to the top, and if they stick to the side, you have to tap them a bit to get them to rise. Nurses do the same before giving a shot or setting up an IV because they don't want air in your blood vessels. If you don't get all the air out of your butterfly syringe, or if you don't put any water in, you will have, instead, a pneumatic system: much less responsive, cushiony motion.

A butterfly's weight is distributed across its body and wings. As the wings move down, the body goes up a bit, and vice versa. The resulting motion is the crazy, fluttery path that a butterfly travels. This toy replicates that motion well.

Thanks to Manuel Hernandez and other staff of the Fresno Community Science Workshop for the remarkable idea of putting hydraulics on a butterfly.

STOMP ROCKETS

The foot goes down, and the rocket goes up.

PARTS	
Plastic bottle (2-liter size works well)	Paper (8½ by 11 or larger)
Bicycle inner tube (10 inch, more or less)	12-inch dowel (¼-inch diameter, for pushing through nose cone)
2-foot PVC tube (more or less), ½- or ¾-inch diameter	
File folders or stiff paper	Yarn (for target)
TOOLS	
PVC cutter (or hacksaw)	

The Basic Concepts

Air gets forced out of the bottle when you reduce the bottle's volume by smashing it. This escaping air pushes the rocket up. After the rocket leaves the tube, it doesn't get pushed anymore. The rocket is going as fast as it will go just as it comes off the tube. It will rise slower and slower until it stops going up altogether; then it will accelerate as it falls back toward the ground.

Build It!

Force the mouth of a plastic bottle into a length of inner tube. Tape it tightly with duct tape.

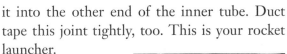

Cut a 2-foot piece of PVC and insert 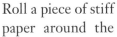 it into the other end of the inner tube. Duct tape this joint tightly, too. This is your rocket launcher.

Roll a piece of stiff paper around the PVC. Make it tight but not so tight that it cannot slide easily up and down the PVC. The paper shown here is being rolled lengthwise, but rolling the other direction to make a longer rocket also works. Add masking tape along the length of the tube to hold the paper closed.

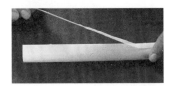

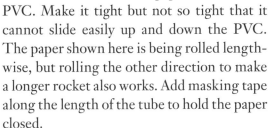

Using a sheet of stiff paper, make at least three fins and glue them on the lower end of the rocket.

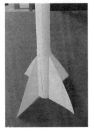

Make a cone from a piece of stiff paper. Tape it tightly.

Insert it into the rocket and cut it off flush. Use the dowel to push the cone through the tube until it sticks out the opposite end.

Pull the cone out until it is just about to pop out of the tube. Position it correctly and hot glue it into position. There should be no holes for air to escape.

Take the rocket outside to launch. Slide the rocket onto the PVC.

Hold the PVC below the rocket and stomp on the bottle. Be careful not to shoot yourself in the face.

Two people can launch very well: one to stomp and one to aim. Lay yarn out in a circle, 5 or 10 feet in diameter, and try to hit this target with rockets from a distance.

More to Think About and Try

⁂ Why do you think the rocket goes up when you stomp on the bottle?
⁂ How does the speed of the rocket as it hits the ground at the end of its flight compare to its speed as it leaves the tube?
⁂ Why might a big bottle work better than a small bottle?
⁂ What do you think would happen if you made the tube a lot longer?

A Little Background

The force that pushes this rocket up comes from the air escaping from the bottle. When you stomp the bottle, its volume decreases. This increases the pressure of the air inside the bottle, and that air takes the only route of escape: out the neck and through the tube. Then it encounters the rocket. It has to push up on the rocket to get out of the launcher tube.

The rocket is pushed for the length of time it is on the PVC tube and then is blown for a few more inches after it comes off. After that there is no more push. In other words, it is less like a rocket and more like a bullet or a ball being thrown. Projectiles that don't have their own energy source accelerate only while they are in contact with their launcher. This is an example of Newton's second law: an object will accelerate according to how much force is put on it, and when the force is no longer there, it will no longer accelerate. The stomp rocket is going as fast as it ever will go just as it comes off the end of the tube. Real rockets will continue to accelerate as long as there is hot gas escaping from their rocket nozzles.

You can divide the motion of the rocket into vertical and horizontal elements. In physics these are called "vectors." If you think about only the vertical element—a flight straight up and straight down—it is easier to understand the motion. As soon as the rocket leaves the tube it has no more force pushing it up, but gravity is always pulling it down. The rocket begins to slow down and continues slowing until it stops at the top of its path. Then, it begins accelerating again toward the ground, this time powered entirely by gravity. If there were no air resistance on the rocket, the speed of the rocket when it hit the ground would be exactly what it was when it left the ground on its way up.

It is harder to consider the sideways vector alone because we have no experience living without gravity or air. If one were to launch this rocket in space, where there is no gravity or air, it would accelerate for the length of the PVC, attain its maximum speed, and then continue on with that speed until it hit something. This is an example of Newton's first law: objects in motion tend to stay in motion and objects at rest tend to stay at rest. Here on Earth, the air that the rocket encounters slows its sideways motion and it always returns to hit the ground and stop.

The result of these two different vectors of motion is a curved path called a "parabola." Everything thrown up from the Earth follows a parabola (if you ignore influence from the air). You can see it in ball games, fireworks blasts, and when you throw a rock.

A bigger bottle would have more air and thus should be able to give more force to the rocket. The longer the tube is, the more air is inside it, and the more air must be pushed. Air is springy (unlike water) and so is the bicycle inner tube, so the longer the tube is, the less directly the air will be pushing on the rocket. With a very long tube, there would be a delay between the stomp of the bottle and the launch of the rocket.

toilet

A fully flushing model of an important modern convenience.

PARTS	
8-inch PVC tube, ½-inch diameter	2 paint paddles
Baseboard	3 two-nail cable clips
Nails (approximately 1¾ inch)	6-inch dowel (⁵⁄₁₆-inch diameter)
Rubber bands	Drinking cup
18-inch clear, flexible tubing (½-inch outer diameter, ⁵⁄₁₆-inch inner diameter)	Toilet-testing dye or food coloring (or liquid watercolor)
Single-size plastic drink bottle, with cap	
TOOLS	
Flapper valve (for demonstration)	PVC cutter (or hacksaw)
Bucket or basin (for testing)	

The Basic Concepts

Water "seeks its level." This means that if two places are connected and full of water, and are open to the atmosphere, the water level will be at the same level at both places.

A trap system is used to keep the air in the sewer from coming into your house, as well as to catch jewelry you accidentally drop in the sink (or toilet).

If your toilet's flapper valve is leaking, you will waste a lot of water and money each year. You can test this with the dye tablets.

Build It!

Cut a length of PVC tubing at least 8 inches long. Place the PVC on the baseboard near one edge and drive two nails into the baseboard, one on each side of the PVC, at both ends of the

baseboard. Hook rubber bands around the nail heads to hold the tubing in place but make it able to slide up and down.

Cut at least 18 inches of flexible tubing. Cut a drink bottle exactly in half through the middle with a knife or pair of scissors. Then, drill a $^{19}\!/_{64}$-inch hole in the bottom of the bottle.

Drill a ½-inch hole in the bottle cap. Insert the flex-

ible tubing a little ways into the hole in the bottle cap. Hot glue around the flexible tubing inside and outside the cap. This joint needs to be watertight.

Glue half a paint paddle perpendicular to the side of the baseboard, along the edge at the bottom, on the end *opposite* the PVC. This should make the toilet model stand up, with the PVC pipe vertical.

Glue a paint paddle vertically to the baseboard, at the opposite end to the PVC, on the opposite *side* of the baseboard. It should be sticking up above the board and be strong enough to support the tank.

Glue the top half of the bottle onto the paint paddle, just above the baseboard, with the cap (and the inserted tubing) pointing down. This is the toilet's bowl. (When gluing anything to a plastic bottle, always put the glue on the other material first; then press the bottle onto the glue. This will avoid deforming the plastic with the heat of the glue.)

Glue the bottom half of the bottle to the top end of the paint paddle so that when the board is standing vertical, the water will drain from it into the bowl. This top half is the toilet's tank.

Hammer a cable clip around the flexible tubing to hold it in position.

Make an S with the tubing so that it ends up inserted into the top of the PVC pipe, facing down. You can use duct tape to secure the flexible tubing into the PVC pipe, but leave a hole so that air can get in. (This hole acts like the vents that go from the drainpipe of a house up through the roof.)

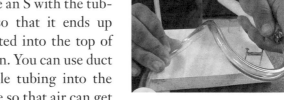

Attach the flexible tubing to the baseboard with cable clips. The cable clips should be horizontally arranged and not hammered in too tightly, so that the tubing is adjustable up and down through them.

Cut at least 6 inches of a $\frac{5}{16}$-inch dowel. Insert it into the tank's hole (from above) as a plug. It should prevent the water from leaking out the hole in the bottom of the water tank. (This dowel acts like the flapper valve in a real toilet.)

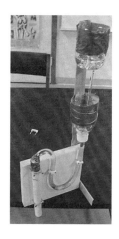

Place the toilet on the edge of a table so that the PVC pipe sticks down, over the edge of the table. Fill the tank with water. Hold a drinking cup under the PVC pipe to catch the water; then pull out the dowel and the toilet should flush.

You can pour the water you collected in the cup back into the tank for another flush. (It takes a couple of flushes to get the air bubbles out of the system.)

To show how dye tablets work, arrange the dowel so that there is a small leak from the tank into the bowl, then put a dye tablet or food coloring into the tank. As it dissolves, the tank water will turn blue, and then the bowl water also will turn blue.

More to Think About and Try

* How could you make the water level in the toilet bowl stay higher?
* How could you make the water flush faster?
* What would make it clog up and not go down?
* How is a real toilet different from this one?

A Little Background

Every sink and toilet in your house has a trap—check for yourself. These S-shaped traps are useful if you drop jewelry down the drain, but the main purpose is to keep the sewer air from coming up into the house. If a big storm, tornado, or hurricane changes the pressure in a house enough, it can push the water out of these traps. The home's residents will know this has happened as the smell of the sewer fills the house.

The water level is the same on both sides of the trap. This is the physical property of water "seeking its level." It happens because gravity pulls the whole mass of water down to its lowest level.

Real toilets have automatic float and valve systems so that the tank is filled again with water after each flush. Toilets also have a somewhat complex device in the tank that fills the bowl to the highest possible level while it is refilling the tank. If you add more water to your toilet bowl you will notice that the level of water in the bowl never rises. This is because every time you add more in the bowl a bit more flows down into the sewer from the back.

So, if your flapper valve is leaking, water from the tank continually leaks into the bowl but the bowl's water level never increases. Thus you may never notice the leak. The float system will periodically spurt a bit more water into the tank, and you may hear this if you are observant. A sure way to test it is to put color dye into the tank (but don't flush!) and wait to see if it appears in the bowl. If it does, you need to replace your flapper valve.

The water level in the toilet bowl can be raised only by making the backside of the trap higher. In a porcelain toilet, this trap level is fixed, but in our model, you just need to raise the PVC to get more water to remain in the bowl after a flush. The size of the hole in a toilet bowl will limit the speed of the flush—if you put in too much water too fast, the bowl will just overflow. Any large object stuck in the hole will clog it up.

ΤORNADO

Better than a ship in a bottle!

PARTS	
Bottle with lid (big is better)	Small pieces of Styrofoam packing
Hobby motor, 1.5–3 volts	Baseboard
2 wires, thin, with insulation	Aluminum foil
Large plastic cup	Film canister (no lid necessary)
Food coloring (or liquid watercolor)	2 C batteries
Glitter	Resistance wire
TOOLS	
Rasp or coarse sandpaper (to roughen up the cap)	Wire strippers

The Basic Concepts

Fluids—liquids or gases (vapors)—flow within the vessel that contains them. Tornados, hurricanes, and whirlpools all have the same sort of motion. In these natural cases the rotation is caused by pressure differences. In this project the rotation is caused by the bottle and the impeller. An impeller throws fluids outward. Propellers throw fluids forward or backward.

Build It!

Make a $^{19}\!/_{64}$-inch hole exactly in the middle of a bottle cap.

Scratch the top of the cap with a rasp so the glue will stick to it better. Then put glue around the hole and press the motor firmly into the hole. Add more glue around the joint between the cap and the motor so that it is very strong. It is important to get this right the first time, because it will not glue well after it gets wet. But be careful not to get any glue inside the cap, on the turning shaft.

Strip both ends of two wires. Connect them to the motor.

Cut at least 1 inch of a hot glue stick. Drill a hole in the end of it with a small nail bit. Cut a slit into the other tip of the glue stick.

Cut a tiny piece of plastic either from the base of your cup or from another bottle, and insert it into the slit. This is the impeller. Push the motor shaft into the hole at the other end of the glue stick.

Fill the bottle about three-quarters full with water. Add a bit of food coloring—too much and you can't see the tornado inside the bottle. A bit of glitter and tiny pieces of Styrofoam are interesting too.

Tightly screw on the cap (with motor attached).

Check out your cup and bottle sizes. Make sure the bottle will sit nicely, cap-and-motor-end down, on the cup, without the motor touching the baseboard. These photos show a small bottle and a large cup. We cut off the bottom of the cup and glued it to the baseboard upside down. For 2-liter-bottle tornados, often the mouth of the cup works to support the bottle, and the cup is glued to the baseboard right side up.

Put a piece of aluminum foil around one end of one wire. Jam the aluminum foil and wire into the bottom of the film canister and glue the film canister to the baseboard.

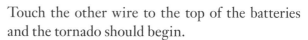

Tape two batteries together and slide one end of them inside the film canister.

Touch the other wire to the top of the batteries and the tornado should begin.

To change the speed of the tornado, connect a piece of resistance wire to the free insulated wire. For full speed, connect the free wire straight to the battery without using the resistance wire. To slow it down, touch the battery with the resistance wire, causing the electricity to pass through a bit of it. The more of the resistance wire the electricity needs to pass through, the slower the motor will go.

More to Think About and Try

* How could you make the tornado spin faster?
* What would happen if you fill the bottle with water so that there is no air in it?
* What would happen if you put the impeller and lid on a different sized bottle?
* Consider a tiny piece of glitter swirling in the tornado: what is its path through the bottle as the tornado spins?

A Little Background

A battery powers this tornado. The sun powers real tornados and all weather patterns. Radiation from the sun warms the Earth differently according to many factors, such as reflectivity of the surface and cloud cover. Hot areas and cold areas then lead to different air pressures. Wind is basically air moving from high to low pressure, and the greater the difference, the stronger the wind. Hurricanes and tornadoes are special situations where a local area of very low pressure (a large area for a hurricane and a small one for a tornado) becomes the center of strong rotating winds.

Why do the winds blow around in circles? Rotation is a common, stable situation in nature. For example, all known planets and their satellites are rotating. For another example, try to shake a bottle of water or soda from side to side, and then hold it still. Invariably, the liquid is rotating when you finish. In technical terms, the winds of hurricanes and tornados are merely conserving their momentum, as all things must.

Adding more batteries will make the motor spin faster; weaker batteries make it spin slower. Changing the size of the impeller is more complex. A very large impeller turns slowly because it has to push a lot of water, and the motor is not strong at slow speeds. A very small impeller turns fast but can push only a tiny bit of water, so it can't get the whole bottle of water moving fast. The optimal size is somewhere in between. The shape also is important. A boat's propeller is much smaller and shaped differently than an airplane's. The best size and shape depend on what kind of fluid is being pushed and at what speed the motor is most efficient.

Changing the wire connections on the battery will make the motor and tornado turn in the opposite direction. In this project, and in most human-made vortexes (whirlpools), your hemisphere is not important; the vortex turns in the direction that you drive it. But your hemisphere is important when considering hurricanes and all large pressure systems. Large low-pressure systems in the Northern Hemisphere turn counterclockwise because they occur on the surface of a spinning sphere—the Earth. The force that makes this happen is called the Coriolis force.

Tornadoes are much smaller and localized than hurricanes. Most often they are formed from the midst of a single thunderstorm and last only minutes. Most in the Northern Hemisphere rotate counterclockwise, but some have been seen to go the other way.

If you put some glitter or bits of paper in the bottle and follow them, you'll see that they are going around and around but also up and down; the up-and-down motion is also circular. They go down near the center of the bottle and back up near the outside. A larger bottle has a similar pattern, just bigger.

eye MODEl

Step inside your eye to see where the light goes.

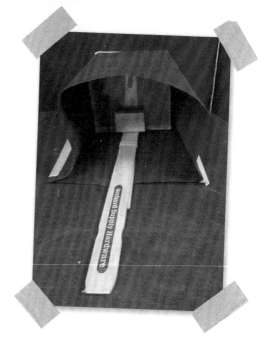

PARTS	
CD case (two transparent sides and black middle insert)	Sheet of black paper (9 inches by 12 inches)
Magnifying glass (small)	Sheet of black paper (12 inches by 18 inches)
2 wood blocks (or film canisters)	
2 paint paddles	Set of colored lights on sockets with power strip
Waxed paper	
Rubber band (small)	

The Basic Concepts

The front surface of the eye is called the cornea. It is hard, and it protects the inside of the eye. The inside back surface of the eye is called the retina. It is made up of nerves that receive the image made by the lens and send the information on to the brain. The eye changes focus to see things far and near. A real eye does this with muscles that change the shape of the lens.

Build It!

Separate the two sides of the CD case and remove the black insert. Use needle-nose pliers or scissors to break off the fringes and widen the hole in the black insert.

Hot glue the magnifying glass to the inside of the black insert.

Pop the black insert back into the transparent cover. This part of the project represents

the cornea (clear case), iris (black insert), pupil (hole), and lens (magnifying glass).

Hot glue a wood block (or film canister) to the end of a paint paddle. Then hot glue the cornea/lens setup to the wood block, with the lens side toward the paint paddle.

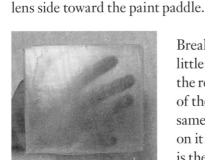

Break off the two little hinge tabs of the remaining side of the CD case. Cut a piece of waxed paper the same size as the case, and tape the waxed paper on it without making any creases or folds. This is the retina.

Hot glue another wood block (or film canister) to the end of another paint paddle. Then hot glue the retina setup to the wood block.

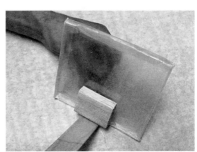

Put the paint paddle with the retina on top of the paint paddle with the cornea/lens. Secure the paddles together with a rubber band, loose enough that they can slide back and forth to vary the distance between the lens and retina.

Now you will enclose this setup with black paper. Begin by applying hot glue to the bottom of the cornea CD case. Then stick this in the center of one end of the small (9-by-12) black paper.

Apply glue to the top edge of the cornea CD case. Stick that to the center of one long edge of the large (12-by-18) black paper.

Wrap the top sheet of paper all the way around until it meets the paper at the bottom. Glue and/or tape all these edges to the case so that light cannot enter. The retina setup should be able to slide back and forth within the enclosure of the black paper.

Tape together the edges of the two black sheets of paper, all the way to the back. Point the model eye to a strong source of light, such as a lightbulb, a window, or a door. Grasp the bottom paint paddle (connected to the cornea/lens and the paper enclosure) with one hand and the top paint paddle (connected to the retina) with the other. Move the retina back and forth until the image is clear.

More to Think About and Try

* How are the models like your eye, and how are they different?
* Why do you need the black paper?
* What happens to the image on the waxed paper if you cover part of the hole letting the light through the lens?
* What if you remove the lens?

A Little Background

Humans gain most information through their eyes. Scientists try hard to understand the eye because sometimes it can trick the brain. This model works well to show the cornea (front half of the CD case), the iris (black plastic insert from CD case), pupil (hole in the black insert), lens (magnifying glass), and retina (other half of the CD case with the waxed paper). The black paper represents the globe of the eyeball but has another function as well.

It is always useful to consider the limitations of a model. In this model, focusing is achieved by moving the lens with respect to the waxed paper. In your eye the lens itself can change shape, thus changing its focal length. In your eye there are two types of transparent fluid: "aqueous humor," between the cornea and lens, and "vitreous humor," filling up the majority of the eye globe between the lens and the retina. There is no one standing behind your eye to report on the image that falls on the retina. The retina is composed of many tiny light-sensitive nerves (the highest concentration of nerves in the body), which are connected to the brain by way of the optic nerve.

If you can obtain a cow's or sheep's eye, you can dissect it to see all these parts. Cut a small hole in the side of the cow eyeball before you start and then shine a light in the pupil. You will be able to see the upside-down image of that light on the retina. Once you remove the lens from a cow's eye, you can use it to project an upside-down image on a piece of paper.

The function of the black paper in this model, and the purpose of the large black cloak used 100 years ago by photographers, is to block out other light in order to see the dim image on the screen (retina). Let's say you are viewing a sunlit stop sign with your eye model. The image you see is made up of light that came from the sun, bounced off the sign, and then entered the eye model through the hole (pupil) and lens. If sunlight were allowed to reach the retina directly, it would overwhelm the dim image of the stop sign.

If you cover part of the pupil, less light gets in, so the image is not as bright. At the same time, it may be clearer because a smaller part of the imperfect lens was traveled across.

The translucent waxed paper serves an important purpose: when an image falls on it, we can view it from either side. Old-time photographers used frosted glass for the same purpose. An image will form on anything placed at the proper distance behind the lens, but most things, such as a piece of white paper, would display the image to viewers only on the lens-side of the paper.

It is possible to build a model like this that would be large enough to seat several people within. The people then sit with their backs to the lens and view the image on a white screen. This is known as "camera obscura." You don't need a lens; you can make one in your own room if you can get it dark enough, and then leave a tiny hole in one window. You'll see the scene outside the window, projected on the opposite wall, only upside down. If you removed the lens from this model and reduced the size of the hole, it would still work, though the image would be much dimmer. This is known as the "pinhole phenomenon," and it is quite interesting in its own right.

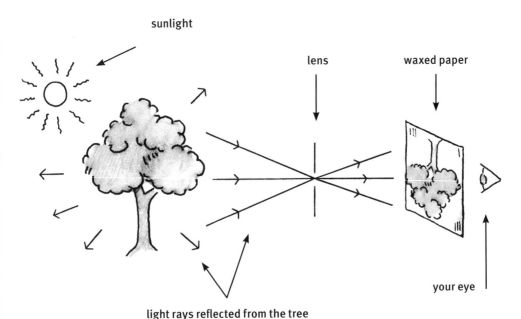

sunlight

lens

waxed paper

your eye

light rays reflected from the tree

Why are the images on the waxed paper upside down and reversed right to left? To understand, we must consider the path of the light from start to finish.

In the drawing on p. 122, the light from the sun hits the tree and is reflected in all directions. If you are viewing the tree with the eye model, a few rays of reflected light will pass into the model through the lens. Lenses bend light as it passes through them, so the light coming from the top of the tree is bent up a bit as it goes through the lens, but still ends up near the bottom of the waxed paper. The light coming from the bottom of the tree is bent down a bit as it goes through the lens, but still ends up near the top of the paper. Meanwhile, the light ray going exactly through the center of the lens does not bend at all and ends up in the center of the paper. The end result is an upside-down image. This happens both on the wax paper of this model and on the retina of your eye.

This same process would happen with just a pinhole and no lens. In that case, however, the light rays would not bend at all.

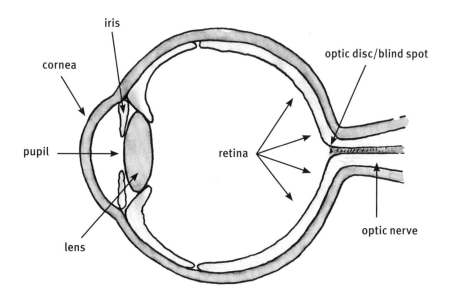

FiNGeRS OF the hAND

These fingers really work. Make four with a thumb and you have a model of a hand!

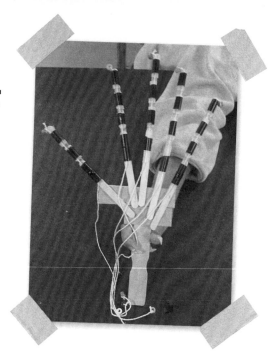

PARTS	
One Finger	
2 craft sticks	Kite string
2 drinking straws (fairly large in diameter)	Bamboo skewer
Bead	
The Whole Hand	
Paint paddle	10 beads
10 craft sticks	Kite string
10 drinking straws (fairly large in diameter)	Bamboo skewer

The Basic Concepts

Craft sticks represent the bones in this project; they give the hand its structure. The strings represent the hand's tendons; they connect the bones to the muscles. And pulling the strings represents the contraction of the muscles. There are actually few muscles in a hand—the muscles in the *arm* pull on the tendons that make a hand move.

Build It!

Note Before Building

You may be frustrated by not being able to finish an entire hand; this takes a long time. To get around this, the instructions below show you how to make a single finger. If you have the stamina, you can build five to complete an entire hand. A single finger is still very nice.

One Finger

Cut a craft stick into three roughly equal pieces. Then cut three lengths of a drinking straw, each slightly shorter than the three cut sticks.

Use hot glue to affix a piece of drinking straw to a craft stick piece. Put the glue on the craft stick, *not* the drinking straw, or the straw may melt. Repeat this for the remaining two pieces.

Glue all three stick segments onto one end of a full drinking straw, but leave a small space in between

each segment so that bending is possible at each joint. The sticks will be sandwiched between the straws when you are finished.

Cut the other end of the full straw, leaving 3 inches to glue onto a full-length craft stick. Glue one more straw segment onto the top of the full-length craft stick in line with the other three segments, as shown.

Tie a bead onto one end of 10-inch-long piece of string. Use a bamboo skewer to push the other end of the string through all four short straw segments.

Tie another bead onto the other end of the string.

Wrap each segment with tape to reinforce the glue. Masking tape works, but black tape looks nicer. Alternatively, you can use only tape and no glue, to avoid burns, but it is harder to hold the small sections in the correct position as you tape them together. Pre-bend the finger at each joint. You have now completed one finger.

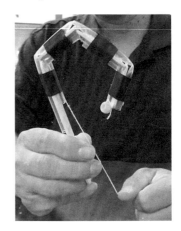

You should be able to hold the long stick and pull the string to make the finger bend.

The Whole Hand

Cut a paint paddle in half; then cut one half into two pieces, one about an inch shorter than the other. Glue the larger piece to the top of the full half of the paint paddle to form a T. Glue the smaller piece just underneath it.

Build three more fingers and a thumb. The thumb has one less segment than the other fingers. Now glue the fingers to the paint paddle frame.

Glue on the thumb toward the side of the hand. Each finger should move when pulling on its string.

More to Think About and Try

* What are some differences between this hand and your hand?
* Human hands have two sets of tendons, one in front of the bones and one in back. What are the ones in back for?
* What happens if your tendons break?
* Ligaments hook bones to other bones. What are the ligaments in this project?

A Little Background

You move your body when your muscles pull on your bones. Ligaments attach bones to bones, and tendons attach bones to muscles. Most of the muscles that pull on each segment of your fingers are actually in your forearm. If you put your hand palm up on the table and move one finger at a time, you can see narrow lengths of muscles move in your forearm. Each of these muscles is connected to one bone in your hand through long tendons. The tendons move from the arm to the hand through the carpel tunnel.

In science, models help you understand the real thing. A model is similar to the real thing, but every model has its limitations. As you work with a model, you must always think about what is similar and what is different from the real thing.

There are several major differences between this model and a real hand. For each of your fingers on your hand, there are actually three muscles,

127

one for each of the three bones. You usually use them all together, so like most people you are probably not able to move a single bone in, say, the tip of a finger. Also, when you stop bending a finger, it doesn't snap back the way a model finger does. You also have another set of muscles and tendons going down the back of each finger to re-extend it on demand.

If a tendon breaks, sometimes a doctor can repair it. Ligaments are much more difficult to heal. The ligaments in this model are the long straws connecting the bones in the back of the finger. Muscles, bones, tendons, and ligaments always work together, and if there is too much force put on the system, any of them may break.

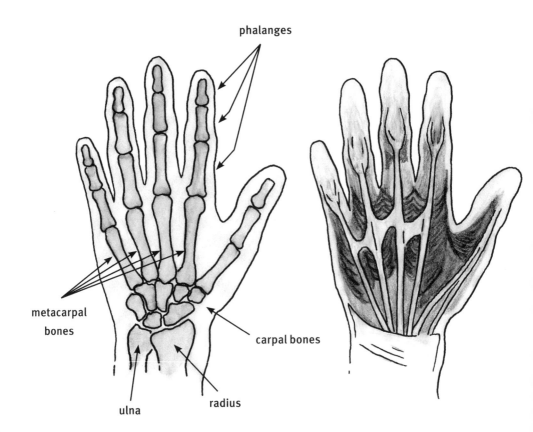

hEARt PUMP

Your life depends on a reciprocating pump just like this.

PARTS	
2 film canisters	1-inch flexible tube (3⁄16-inch outer diameter, to fit snugly into long one)
Film canister lid	
Single-size plastic drink bottle (no lid necessary)	1-inch flexible tube into which the long one fits snugly (5⁄16-inch inner diameter, 1⁄2-inch outer diameter)
7-inch bicycle inner tube (1 1⁄4-inch diameter works well; film canister must fit completely inside it)	String
	Red food coloring (or liquid watercolor)
2 pennies	
18-inch flexible tube (3⁄16-inch inner diameter, 5⁄16-inch outer diameter)	
TOOLS	
Sandpaper	

The Basic Concepts

The heart is a muscle that pumps blood through the body and back, then through the lungs and back. Pumps like the two in your heart have two one-way valves, so that the liquid can go in only one direction. The human heart has four chambers: two that work together to pump blood to the lungs and two that work together to pump blood to the rest of the body. Birds have only two chambers, like this model.

Build It!

Drill ¹⁹⁄₆₄-inch holes in the bases of two film canisters and one film canister lid. Check to be sure there are no burrs or rough edges around the holes inside of the film canisters. (The pennies must be able to lay flat across the holes.)

Drill another ¹⁹⁄₆₄-inch hole in the bottom of the bottle halfway between the center and the edge. Change to the ½-inch bit and enlarge the bottle's hole. (The bottle often rips if you drill directly with the ½-inch bit.)

Cut 7 inches of bicycle inner tube. Push one of the film canisters into the center of the inner tube.

Tape this film canister in tightly with black tape.

Pull the inner tube over the mouth and neck of the bottle as far as it will go. The film canister within

the inner tube should be with its mouth up. Tape this joint tightly with black tape. The bottle and inner tube up to this first film canister represent the atrium. Blood gathers here as it arrives back at the heart.

Drop a penny into the film canister within the inner tube. This will be the first valve, between the atrium and ventricle.

Push the second film canister into the top of the inner tube, almost to the rim. Drop another penny into it. This will be the second valve, between the ventricle and the body. The short length of inner tube between the two film canisters represents the ventricle. This is the chamber that does most of the pumping.

Cap the film canister. Tape the inner tube tightly to this film canister and tape its lid on.

Prepare your flexible tubing. Cut 1-inch pieces from each of three sizes, then a 17-inch piece from the medium-diameter tubing. Sand the short pieces of

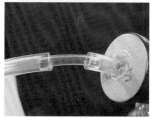

large-diameter and medium-diameter tubing so that they are rough all over. This will make the hot glue stick to them better. The tubing collectively represents all the vessels in the body.

Hot glue the short medium-diameter piece into the hole in the film canister lid. Insert the small-diameter piece into the short medium-diameter piece.

Stick the 17-inch piece over the small-diameter piece. When you take apart this joint later, the small-diameter piece should remain stuck in the piece glued to the film canister lid. This will be your squirter. (You could also drill a smaller hole into the film canister lid and insert the small-diameter piece directly. The way it is shown here requires only two drill bits.) Sand the bottle around the hole in the base, again to make the hot glue stick better.

Insert the large-diameter piece into this hole and hot glue it in. Do a good job on this joint because once the glue is wet, it will no longer stick. Examine it for tiny holes and add more glue until you are sure it won't leak. (If it does leak, the project still works—you will just get wet as it works.)

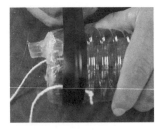

Cut about 24 inches of string and tie knots at both ends. Tape them so that the loop extends over the bottom of the bottle.

Put the loop over your neck to hold the pump when you're not using

it. Fill the pump through the large tube in the base with water until it is almost completely full. You will need to hold the long tube up, or the water will leak out as you are filling it. This process is easiest done at a sink.

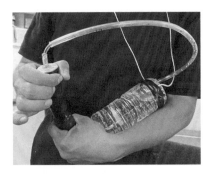

Cradle the bottle in one arm and grasp the inner film canister with that hand. Grasp the outer film canister with the other. Begin a systematic pumping action, first pulling the two film canisters apart, then pushing them firmly back together. The film canisters should be more or less vertical as you do this, to make the penny valves work properly. You should be able to see and feel the water being pumped around the tubing and into the base of the bottle again. This is the heart model working. Color the water red for an added effect.

To convert the heart pump into a squirt gun, remove the long tube from the smallest piece and fire away.

More to Think About and Try

* How could you make the pump stronger?
* Where would the lungs be in this system?
* When you push the two film canisters together and that part of the inner tube gets smashed smaller, what happens to the other part?
* What would happen if there was a hole in the thin tubing?

A Little Background

When talking about the function of the heart, it is important to consider the lungs at the same time. The importance of the heart and lungs can be seen from their position in the body. They are behind the rib cage and thus are protected more than any other organ aside from the brain. If you damage your heart or lungs, you'll die in minutes, whereas if you damage your other organs, you'll have more time on your side.

The function of the heart and lungs (along with the entire circulatory and respiratory systems) is to supply each cell in the body with oxygen and nutrients and also to remove waste materials and carbon dioxide. Both organs work involuntarily; that is, you don't have to think about them. You keep breathing and your heart keeps pumping even while you're sleeping. The heart is a muscle that is controlled by tiny electric signals.

It is always useful to think about where a scientific model is accurate and where it breaks down. In this heart pump model, the inner tube section between the two film canisters is like the ventricle. It does most of the pumping. The bottle and the other inner tube section are like the atrium; they receive the water when it comes back from the tube. You can watch this section of the inner tube get bigger and smaller in opposition to the one that you are pumping. The clear tube is like the blood vessels. As the blood flows away from the heart, it is in vessels called arteries, so the first part of the tube is like the arteries. Blood then flows into smaller and smaller vessels, which are called capillaries and which lead to every cell in the body. Finally, blood starts back to the heart in vessels called veins. So, the tube is like a vein as it flows back into the bottle. If there was a hole in the tubing, the water would be pumped out of the system. This is similar to when a person loses blood.

There are several things missing from the heart model. There is only one short blood vessel. Even a tiny animal's system of blood vessels is extraordinarily complex as it connects up with each cell in the body. Also, even in a bird's heart, which has only two chambers, there are two different routes for the blood: one through the lungs and one to the rest of the body. Our heart model doesn't represent lungs at all (though a lung model follows this project); there would need to be an entirely separate pump with valves and tubes running to the lungs.

The penny valves are very simple models of a real heart's valves. As the water comes into the first film canister, it blasts the penny out of the way. Then, as the ventricle chamber is compressed, the pressure rises and the water pushes that penny back down to cover the hole. But the penny in the other film canister is blasted up, allowing the water to go in only one direction. When the ventricle is expanded again, that penny is sucked back down to cover that hole while the penny in the first film canister is blasted up again allowing water to flow in. This is the way most reciprocating pumps work.

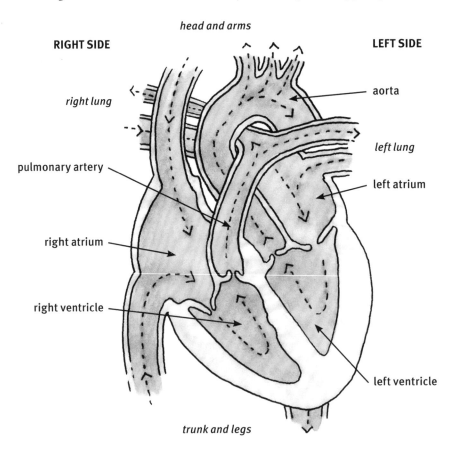

LUNG MODEL

Breathe deep as you inflate a balloon inside a bottle.

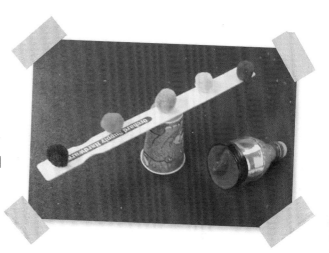

PARTS	
Single-size plastic drink bottle (no lid necessary; soda bottles are stronger and work better than water bottles)	Craft pom-poms
	Paint paddle
	Cup
2 balloons	

The Basic Concepts

Lungs are basically sacks full of many smaller sacks, all connected together like branches of a tree. Air passes through the mouth and into these sacks, and blood circulates in the walls. Carbon dioxide is transferred from the blood to the air, and oxygen is transferred from the air to the blood.

Lungs are not muscles. The diaphragm is the muscle that moves up and down and draws air into the lungs. In this project the balloon over the bottom half of the bottle is like the diaphragm.

Build It!

Cut a plastic bottle in half. Cut the mouth and neck off a balloon; then stretch the remaining half over the bottom of the bottle. It helps to have someone hold the bottle while you do this. If you do it right, the bottle will not collapse on itself. This balloon represents the diaphragm.

Tape the balloon to the bottle.

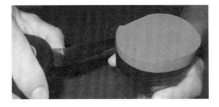

Stuff another balloon in through the mouth of the bottle. Wrap the mouth of the balloon over the mouth of the bottle. This balloon represents a lung.

To make your model exhale, push the diaphragm up into the bottle. The lung balloon will shrink. To make it inhale, pull down on the diaphragm. The lung balloon will expand.

When you are done experimenting with your lung model, take out the lung balloon, and you will have an air gun. Set up a shooting range with a cup and paint paddle. Place small objects such as craft pom-poms on top and try to knock them off. Pull back on the diaphragm and let it go. The gun also works well for blowing out candles.

More to Think About and Try

* What happens to your diaphragm when you take a very deep breath?
* Why do you think the heart is made of muscle but the lung is not?
* Why can some people hold their breath longer than others?
* If you breathe into a bag without letting any air escape, after a minute or so you start feeling like you're not getting any air, even though you're breathing normally. What is going on?

A Little Background

To fully understand how your lungs work within your body, reread the previous project's background on the heart. Unlike your heart, your lungs are not muscles—they can't move by themselves. The diaphragm muscle makes them work. This muscle is a bit different from the heart in that you can consciously control your diaphragm for a few minutes, such as when you hold your breath or blow out a candle. But as soon as you forget about it, it goes back to working on its own.

The lung model in this project is very simple, and surprisingly accurate. The top balloon is like your lungs: it inflates when the bottom balloon, which is similar to the diaphragm, is lowered. The bottle itself is like the rib cage, protecting the lungs. It would be more accurate if there were two lungs instead of one, if there was a heart in there with the lungs, if there were blood vessels connected to the balloons, and if the balloons were actually composed of millions of tiny balloons.

Different people have different sized lungs, and different people use oxygen at different rates. Pearl divers can have lungs much larger than usual, the result of breathing very deep in order to raise their oxygen capacity and maximize their time under water. If you breathe into a bag, you will soon convert all the oxygen in that volume of air into water and carbon dioxide. You need oxygen to live, so your body will begin to give you signals that you need more.

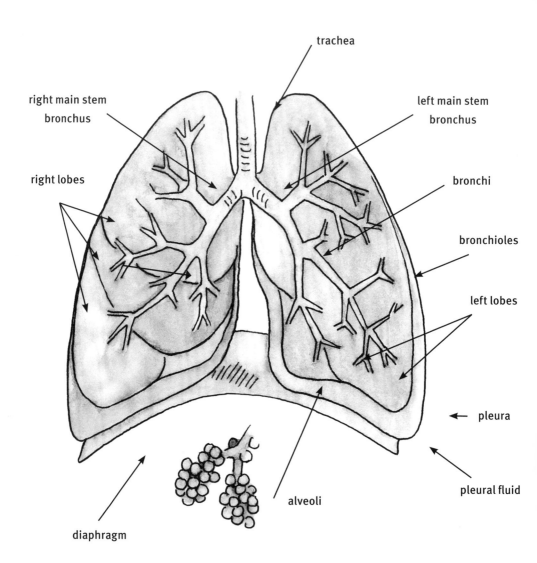

trachea

right main stem
bronchus

left main stem
bronchus

right lobes

bronchi

bronchioles

left lobes

pleura

pleural fluid

alveoli

diaphragm

CARTESIAN DIVERS

Density determines whether they float or sink.

PARTS	
2 drinking straws (transparent or translucent)	2-liter bottle with lid
	Thin wire (for making hoop in bottle)
4 rubber bands (small)	Piece of Styrofoam packing material
6 paper clips (small)	
Large pitcher, bottle, or bucket with open top (for testing)	

The Basic Concepts

Things float when they are less dense than the fluid surrounding them. Things sink when they are denser than the fluid surrounding them. Knowing either the weight or size (volume) alone is not enough to determine whether something will sink or float. You have to know both, and that will tell you the density. (Something small may sink, but something big may float, whether it be liquid or solid.)

When you squeeze the bottle in this project, the air inside gets pressed into a smaller space. The space the water takes up doesn't change. Because of that, some water goes into the straw, making it heavier. Since the straw's size (volume) did not change, its density increased.

Build It!

Cut a 5- or 6-inch piece of drinking straw. Fold a little bit back from one end and wrap a rubber band very tightly around the doubled portion. To make it very tight, wrap only half  the rubber band, then fold the end of the straw again and wrap the rest of the rubber band so that the rubber band holds down two folds, as shown. Slide several paper clips inside the open end of straw. This is your first diver; make at least one more.

 Test the divers in an open vessel. For a diver to work, it must have enough weight so that it just barely floats. When you tap it from above, it should sink and then rise again slowly. If it sinks and doesn't come back up, you have too many paper clips. Add or subtract paper clips until the divers work correctly.

When they work, drop the divers in a bottle almost full of water and cap it tightly. Squeeze the bottle, and the divers should sink. Release it, and they should rise. Look at the straw very carefully to see what is happening to make the diver sink and rise.

To make a game with the divers, add a wire hoop to the bottle. Wrap a length of wire around a Styrofoam packing peanut. At the other end make a loop that is just small enough to fit through the mouth of the

bottle. The loop should be perpendicular to the rest of the wire so that the divers can go down through it. The wire hoop assembly should be just shorter than the height of the water in the bottle. Drop it into the bottle.

When you squeeze the bottle, try to get the diver to pass through the loop on its way to the bottom.

More to Think About and Try

* What happens inside the straw diver when you squeeze the bottle?
* Why do you think the diver goes down?
* What would happen if you filled the diver bottle only half full?
* Could you make the straw diver go down even if the bottom of the straw were sealed off?

A Little Background

Throw a small grain of sand into the ocean, and it will sink. Throw an enormous tree in, and it will float. What matters is not the weight (or mass) or the size (or volume), but the amount of mass in a given volume. That is the definition of "density." It is easiest to think about if you hold one of these constant. For example, if you have two identical bottles, one full of sand and one full of air, their volumes are the same, but since the mass is different, the densities are different. A little piece of wood would have less mass than the same sized little piece of sand. It would take many cups of Styrofoam packing pieces to equal the weight of one cup of water because the water is denser.

Density is a property of all materials. You can compare the density of a solid and a fluid by checking to see if the solid floats. Floating is the opposite of sinking, and sinking is just gravity pulling something down. You could even say that we have all sunk to the bottom of the atmosphere. This is because we all have densities greater than the gas that makes up the atmosphere.

Think of all the things that you have seen float or sink. It is all due to different densities: Helium and hot air balloons are less dense than air, so they float. Bubbles are less dense than water, so they float. Boats are less dense than water, so they float unless they are filled with water, in which case they usually become denser than water and sink. Ice is less dense than water, so it floats. Sugar is denser than water, so it sinks until it dissolves, at which time it has made the water itself denser.

In this Cartesian divers toy, the straw floats when it is less dense than water and sinks when it is denser than water. Its density changes when you squeeze the bottle. Air is made of gasses, and gas molecules are farther apart than liquid molecules. If you press on them, they will get closer together. Liquid and solid molecules are close together already, and if you press on them, nothing much happens. You can feel this by squeezing on two identical bottles, one all full of air and the other completely full of water.

If you look very carefully at the bottom end of the straw when you squeeze the Cartesian diver bottle, you'll see water going up into it. If you look at the top of the water in the bottle, you may also notice it move up a bit in the neck when you squeeze. This is because all the air trapped in the bottle is compressed when you squeeze and the water is not. The water moves up to take the place of the air.

When water enters the straw, the straw's mass goes up while its volume stays the same, so its density goes up, too. When its density gets larger than that of water, it will sink. If the bottom of the straw were sealed off, it would still move down when you squeezed the bottle. The straw would be squashed a bit as you squeezed. Now the diver's mass would not change but its volume would decrease, making its density increase.

It is unclear how Cartesian divers got their name. The word "Cartesian" generally refers to something connected to the great scientist/philosopher/mathematician René Descartes (1596–1650), but in fact it was a student of another pioneering scientist, Galileo, who originally described this toy in 1648. See www.ed.uiuc.edu/courses/CI241-science-Sp95/resources/philoToy/philoToy.html for more information.

Oil ON WATER

Density works the same way with two liquids.

PARTS	
Single-size plastic drink bottle, with cap	3 film canisters
Water	Bamboo skewer
10 ounces oil, any transparent type	Plastic bag
Food coloring (or liquid watercolor)	Baseboard
TOOLS	
Funnel	Long stick or tweezers
Nail, large (to make hole for boat's mast)	Stapler with staples

The Basic Concepts

Like solids, liquids float and sink depending on their densities. The density of a material does not depend on how much of it is present, so a tiny drop of one liquid will act the same as a large quantity when added to another liquid.

In this project, the water is denser than the boat, which is denser than the oil.

Build It!

Pour water into a small plastic bottle until it is just under half full. Then add oil until it is almost full. Lastly, add several drops of food coloring and watch what happens.

 Make a small boat to float inside the bottle. Cut the hull of the boat from a plastic film canister. The boat's hull must be small enough to fit through the mouth of the bottle. Place the hull on top of a film canister lid and punch a hole in the center with a nail.

Cut a small piece of bamboo skewer for the boat's mast. Carefully cut a small slit in one end of the bamboo piece.

Next, cut a piece of a plastic bag for a flag and insert it into the slit.

 Insert the mast into the hole in the hull.

Put the boat into the bottle. If it doesn't sink to the water, fish it out with a long stick or tweezers and put a staple into it. Before capping the bottle tightly, fill it all the way to the top with either water or oil. It looks best without an air bubble.

 To make a stand for your project, hot glue a film canister to a baseboard.

Then cut the bottom off another film canister, and cut it down one side. Glue it to the top of the other canister, so that it opens up to receive the bottle. Balance the bottle on the stand.

The boat should float in the center.

More to Think About and Try

* What would happen if you made a boat entirely out of wood and put it in the bottle of oil and water?
* What about a boat made of wire?
* If you put a drop of water in a bucket of oil, would it sink or stay on top?
* How about a drop of oil in a bucket of water?

A Little Background

Density is a property of all materials, whether they are solid, liquid, or gas. Two liquids or two gases together will find their places according to their density, just like a solid in a liquid. In this project, water sinks below the oil because it is denser. The food coloring is water-based, not oil-based, so it sinks through the oil without coloring it, yet mixes well when it hits the water.

The boat also sinks in the oil, but then floats on the water. If your mast is too large it may decrease the density of the boat so much that it floats on the top of the oil. Adding staples increases the density, because metal is denser than any of the other materials used.

If you made a boat from wood or Styrofoam, it would probably float above the oil as well. On the other hand, a boat made from wire would likely sink beneath the water. Try both and see!

Density is defined as the amount of mass in a given volume. This doesn't change if you cut something in half or otherwise reduce the *amount* of it. As you observed, a drop of water will move to the bottom of a pool of oil, just as a drop of oil will remain on top of a bucket of water.

GAK AND OOBLECK

Renegade materials on the loose!

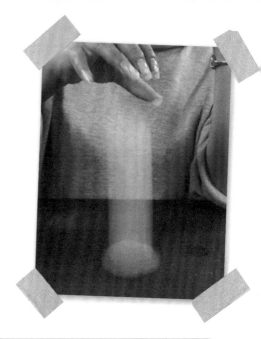

PARTS	
Gak	
Borax	About 2 ounces glue
Large plastic cup for Borax solution	Food coloring (or liquid watercolor)
Film canister, no lid	Paint paddle
Short clear plastic cup	Ziploc bag
Oobleck	
About 2 ounces cornstarch	Food coloring (or liquid watercolor)
Short clear plastic cup	

The Basic Concepts

Some things are not exactly a liquid and not exactly a solid. Both Gak and Oobleck act like solids if you move them fast, but act like liquids if you let them move slowly.

Gak is a polymer, meaning it has long molecules that can slide back and forth beside one another while still holding together. Oobleck is a mixture of a liquid and tiny particles of a solid. The solid particles in Oobleck are normally lubricated by the liquid and slide together smoothly, but when Oobleck is pressed, the solid particles rub against one another and move less fluidly.

Two substances may just blend together when they combine, forming a mixture, or a chemical reaction may take place between them, creating one or more new substances. The substances created in a chemical reaction may have very different properties than either of the original two substances.

Build It!

Gak

Put some borax in a large cup, about a half-inch in the bottom. Fill the cup up with water.

Stir with paint paddle to make a borax solution. The undissolved borax at the bottom is evidence that the liquid on top is a saturated solution. Once the liquid borax solution has been used up (in the steps below), add more water and stir again to get more solution.

Pour one film canister of glue into a short cup. Add a film canister of water to the glue.

Add a few drops of coloring. Mix these three ingredients together with a paint paddle.

Add a film canister of the borax solution. Stir it all together. The chemical reaction takes place in this step. Remove the Gak from the cup and play with it. It will get drier as you play.

When you are done playing, put it in a Ziploc bag. (Gak can be very messy on fabrics.) Write on the Ziploc bag how many cans of glue, water, and borax solution you put in. Then make another batch, but instead of using a 1 to 1 to 1 mixture, change one of the variables to see what happens, or change the order of adding the different ingredients.

You can do many experiments with Gak to learn its strange properties. For example, put the Gak near the edge of a table and wait to see what happens.

Put the Gak inside different objects, such as a film canister. As you squish it in, listen to the interesting noises it makes. Or put the Gak on top of a cup and see what happens to it.

Stretch your Gak to see how far it goes; then measure it.

Oobleck

Put cornstarch in a short cup. Add a tiny bit of water and mix them together.

Add more water bit by bit until something interesting begins to happen.

Play with it: poke it, stir it, hit it, squeeze it, pick it up, pour it. You can also add food coloring.

More to Think About and Try

❋ What is the longest you can pull your Gak without breaking it?

❋ What happens if you just leave your Gak sitting on the edge of a table?

❋ What do you think would happen if you got your Gak warmer or froze it?

❋ How could you make your Oobleck harder?

A Little Background

Most people learn the three states of matter: solid, liquid, and gas. This is only a part of the picture. First of all, scientists believe most (over 90 percent) of the visible universe is made up of none of these but rather a fourth state called "plasma." Most of the visible mass of the universe is contained in stars. Stars are powered by nuclear reactions so hot that the basic structure of atoms changes. The result is a state of matter called plasma, which is very hot and has a different distribution of electric charge. This situation is created for some electronic devices (plasma balls, plasma screens) and occurs naturally here on Earth in the form of lightning and other spark discharges.

The substances in this activity straddle the line between solid and liquid. Gak does so because of its long polymer molecules sliding past one another like wet noodles. Oobleck has this property because the shape of the cornstarch particles allows water between them. The water can act as a lubricant and aid the particles in slipping beside one another. When you push hard and fast, however, the particles themselves touch and don't slip nearly as easily. A similar situation can exist in wet sand. You may have noticed the water being pressed out of wet sand if you have ever walked on a shore. Wet sand has properties very different from dry sand.

Oobleck is just a mixture. If you let the water evaporate, you have the original cornstarch again. If you let your ball of Gak dry out, you have dry Gak—nothing at all like the glue or borax you put in. Chemicals in the glue and borax reacted to give a fundamentally different substance. If you make some Gak without color and then add the food coloring, the ball of Gak will not take in the color. The reaction has already happened, and the new substance does not absorb the watery food coloring.

Gak made with more water tends to be gooier, and with less water tends to be harder. Making Gak with no water aside from that in the glue and borax solution can give you a tight substance that bounces like a rubber ball. But leave that ball on the table for a few hours and it "spills" like milk; it behaves like a liquid over long periods of time. Play with the variables in the recipe, and you'll learn more than if you simply follow the recipe exactly.

bRinGinG these PRoJects into the CIASSROOM

THESE PROJECTS WERE ORIGINALLY done in Watsonville, California, with groups of 20 students from the third through eighth grades, once a week, in their after-school program. In fall 2007, we entered our fifth year with this program, serving around 400 students per week. Ours continues to be one of the most popular after-school activities in our district. Students love our projects because they are free to experiment and tinker with real stuff, and teachers love them because the students learn just by constructing the projects.

It is a tremendous irony that in this book we have mapped out these projects in a step-by-step, cookbooklike manner. When we teach the projects, we never give detailed instructions. We bring two working models for the students to study, and we explain only the basic gist of how to build a project. We then go over any very difficult or intricate parts and all safety issues. We also give a hint as to the science involved by asking two focus questions, though we do not discuss any answers at first. After an introduction of 10 minutes or so we pass out the materials and everyone starts building. We spend the bulk of our class time constructing the project.

Toward the end of the class, the students are (with great difficulty) drawn back to their seats for a short discussion on the content of the projects. We generally discuss answers to the focus questions, but often we also discuss other concepts that arose as the students completed their projects. Middle school students are also required to do a short write-up at the end, explaining what they have done and learned and writing answers to the focus questions.

We are careful never to do any part of the project for the student. The question asked most often is, "What do I do now?" to which the answer is "Go look at the model." To learn to follow a model as opposed to detailed directions is something rare and valuable in school culture. There are great benefits to this pedagogy: The teacher is not so necessary, which empowers the student toward lifelong self-learning and allows the teacher to focus on certain individual students' needs. Students can be creative and build the project according to their own tastes, and they can build at different paces as well, with those who finish first helping others or continuing to build more onto their project.

Tools and Materials

Each project uses many and varied materials. A great effort has been made to rely on free and recycled materials, such as plastic drink bottles and cans, film canisters, scrap wood, and paint-stirring paddles. Local sources for these materials can be found easily. Certain special materials—less than 5 percent—need to be acquired from specialty sources: electronics supply stores, science supply stores, and so forth. Nearly all of the parts can be found at the sources listed here:

Retail Sources

* Hardware or home improvement shops
* Office supply stores
* Grocery stores
* Craft shops
* Discount, dollar, or 99-cent stores
* Electronics shops such as Radio Shack (motors, battery snaps, magnets, audio plugs, wire, amplifiers)

Online Sources

* Air-Tite Products, Inc.; www.air-tite.com (syringes)
* Allmagnetics; www.allmagnetics.com (magnets)

* Discount School Supply; www.discountschoolsupply.com (paper, beads, glitter, paint, plastic eyes, craft sticks, pipe cleaners, craft pom-poms, liquid watercolor—much cheaper than common food coloring)
* Kelvin; www.kelvin.com (motors, battery snaps, magnets)
* Mouser Electronics; www.mouser.com (audio plugs, battery snaps)
* Oriental Trading Company; www.orientaltrading.com (magnifying glasses)
* Tap Plastics; www.tapplastics.com (mirrors)

Scrap and Donation Sources

* Bike shops (inner tubes)
* Cabinet shops or lumber yards (wood pieces)
* Photo shops (film canisters)
* Paint shops (paint paddles)
* Phone company yards (wire)
* Radio stations (CDs and CD cases)
* Recycling centers (bottles, cans)
* Restaurants (egg cartons, bottle caps, straws)
* Secondhand stores (wool, motorized toys for motors, wheels, and so forth)

A significant amount of time will be spent gathering and preparing these materials; therefore, it is far more efficient to gather many materials and deliver the projects to several different groups. If many students are to be served, good storage systems are important and a table saw is very useful for preparing small wood pieces from larger scraps of wood.

These toys have been used as the sole curriculum in our Students Teaching Project. We use the Watsonville Environmental Science Workshop to prepare and store the materials. Teams of three teach the projects: one lead teacher (college student or college graduate) and two high school students. These "Teacher-Students" meet once a week to learn the following week's project and prepare the materials. Naturally, more staff is better when doing hands-on projects with a group of students, but when high school helpers are not available, our lead teachers routinely teach the classes by themselves as well.

About the Watsonville Environmental Science Workshop

THE WATSONVILLE ENVIRONMENTAL SCIENCE Workshop is located within the Community Center at Marinovich Park in Watsonville, California. It was founded in 1997 with a seed grant from the National Science Foundation and is one of 12 such programs nationwide.

Our community science Workshop is not only an after-school program but also a unique community resource. Our Workshop complements the science and math education our students get from school and allows them to pursue the technical areas of their own interests. Our Workshop also gives community kids the opportunity to interact together in a rich, stimulating, and safe environment with adults present who care about their development in academics as well as their development as a whole person.

The core of our program is the open-structure, open-door Workshop hours. After school and on Saturdays, community kids and their families are free to come and construct the projects of their imaginations. While they are at the Workshop, they can peruse our exhibits and project models in addition to working on whatever project they choose to construct. They learn to use tools and a plethora of different materials. In this natural way, students can learn science, math, and engineering from direct experience. They get the opportunity to learn through inquiry, exploration, and peer consultation. The competence they gain builds true confidence. All the while, they are subconsciously defining "science" for themselves, and the definition involves fun and success. All of this is markedly different from what most of them get in school.

In addition to the core program, we take our most popular hands-on science projects to about 20 local school sites through our Students

Teaching program, in which adults and high school students team up to do the teaching. The S. H. Cowell Foundation has given us generous support for the Students Teaching Project. Three alternative high schools bring their classes to the Workshop once a week for a formal hands-on science lesson, complete with notes and write-up. Several field trips and camping trips each year get students out into the local environment. We work closely with the other environmental education programs of the City of Watsonville. Teachers frequent the Workshop for informal consultations on how to succeed with hands-on lessons for their classes, and we occasionally do mass teacher training as well.

Everything we do employs recycled, reclaimed, and scrap objects, so that students are made firmly aware of the value and potential of the materials around them. Conservation principles are conveyed, as is the presence of science in everyday life: students become aware that science is everywhere, not just in special labs and kits. In addition, this practice keeps our costs low and our Workshop sustainable. We are always on the lookout for donations of interesting junk.

For more information, please see our Web page: www.ci.watsonville.ca.us/scienceworkshop.

iNDEX